WALKER SUN BOOKS

SB- 1 *Islam* by Dominique Sourdel
SB- 2 *Africa Before the White Man* by Henri Labouret
SB- 3 *War* by Gaston Bouthoul
SB- 4 *Buddhism* by Henri Arvon
SB- 5 *The Nature of Hinduism* by Louis Renou
SB- 6 *The Essence of Ancient Philosophy* by André Cresson
SB- 7 *A History of Alchemy* by Serge Hutin
SB- 8 *Surrealism* by Yves Duplessis
SB- 9 *The Churches of the West* by Marcel Pacaut
SB-10 *A History of Judaism* by André Chouraqui
SB-11 *A History of Magic* by Jérôme-Antoine Rony
SB-12 *Socrates* by Jean Brun
SB-13 *Hitler's Germany* by Claude David
SB-14 *Sexual Reproduction* by Louis Gallien
SB-15 *Memory and Forgetting* by Jean-Claude Filloux
SB-16 *Aerodynamics* by Jacques Lachnitt
SB-17 *Psychoanalysis* by Daniel Lagache
SB-18 *Longevity* by Jacques Guillerme
SB-19 *The Psychology of Animals* by Jean-Claude Filloux
SB-20 *Probability and Certainty* by Emile Borel
SB-21 *Nuclear Radiations* by Marc Lefort
SB-22 *The Earth and the Moon* by Jean Taillé
SB-23 *The Origins of Life* by Jules Carles
SB-24 *Animal Migration* by René Thévenin
SB-25 *Russian Literature* by Marcelle Ehrhard
SB-26 *Chinese Literature* by Odile Kaltenmark
SB-27 *Indian Literature* by Louis Renou
SB-28 *A History of Asia* by René Grousset
SB-29 *A History of Byzantium* by Paul Lemerle
SB-30 *Life in the Middle Ages* by Geneviève d'Haucourt

WALKER SUN BOOKS

*continued*

SB-31 *Matter, Electricity and Energy* by Geneviève Darmois

SB-32 *Cosmic Rays* by André Cachon, Alice Daudin and Louis Jauneau

SB-33 *Hypnosis and Suggestion* by Paul Chauchard

SB-34 *Microbes* by André Boivin

SB-35 *Genetics and Heredity* by Maurice Caullery

SB-36 *Biological Rhythms* by Alain Reinberg and Jean Ghata

SB-37 *A History of Biology* by Maurice Caullery

SB-38 *Race and Human Migrations* by Louis Dollot

SB-39 *Language and Thought* by Paul Chauchard

SB-40 *The Origin of Species* by Emile Guyénot

# *Language and Thought*

DR. PAUL CHAUCHARD

*Director of the School for Higher Studies*

Translated from the French by Noel Kenton

A SUN BOOK

*Walker and Company · New York*

*First published in France as Le Langage et La Pensée,*
*a title in the Que sais-je? series.* © *1956,*
*Presses Universitaires de France.*



*Published simultaneously in Canada by*
*George J. McLeod, Limited, Toronto.*
*Library of Congress Catalog Card Number: 64-18459*

*Manufactured in the United States of America*
*from type set in Austria.*

# *Contents*

Part Three: Man without Speech

# *Introduction*

**In the Beginning was the Word.**
*The Gospel of St. John I. i*
**Language is the actuality of thought.**
*Karl Marx*

When man, more anxious and disquieted than ever before in the face of an enormous increase in his powers, and wanting to take full responsibility for his past, present and future use of them, seeks to know and understand himself—to apply himself afresh to the eternal questions—he does not find any basically new message in the objective sources of information on his nature, such as biology and its kindred sciences. The zoological term *Homo sapiens* implies in effect that man, as regards his classification in the animal series, is identifiable by his ability to think and reflect, to imagine and reason abstractly. Nevertheless students of animal psychology can see that human thought, in spite of its complexity, is no more than an evolutionary extension of something that exists germinally in inferior species. Today it is apparent that the mind, as manifested at the lower levels of life and in the most primitive of creatures, is far more complex than was realized by the first scientific observers. When, in this connection, we consider birds and mammals—and more especially the higher mammals such as the anthropoid apes or those such as the dog and the cat that have been brought into contact with human problems by domestication—we do not do so with anthropomorphic intent, but merely to assert their closeness to us as scientifically recognized; and indeed *Homo sapiens* cannot segregate himself in splendid isolation, since he is not the only intelligent being in the world of animal mechanisms. Nevertheless a critical level of great complexity is attained by the mere fact of acquiring human status, and from this arise such far-reaching changes and potentialities that it becomes legitimate to speak of an actual difference of nature.

What has led to an underestimation of the thinking powers of animals is that we can only know about them from outside, and a great deal of experimentation involving the use of various tests is necessary before it can be proved that the often excessive claims of "animal lovers" have some foundation. When we observe the intelligent, comprehending expressions of a dog or a chimpanzee we are tempted to say that the animal only lacks words to express its thoughts, and this, for those who seek to understand the true nature of human thought, takes us to the heart of the problem: only man is capable of a genuine language, enabling him to communicate his thought to his own kind. Although language originates as a means of communication especially necessary for the cooperation of a social species, it must not be separated from thought to become only a tool in the mind's service—a tool whose absence alone prevents the higher mammals from communicating their thoughts in a way analogous to ours. In man language has at once an *external* form that enables us to communicate with each other, and an *internal* form that affirms our thought, that is, our reflective consciousness. An animal thinks, but its thought process differs from ours both in its nature and in the degree to which it can be made known to the world, and the animal's consciousness is different because it is not, and cannot be, expressed in words. A man deprived of language, or one whose power of language is rudimentary, is not disconcerted only in his relationship with others, but his thought process itself is restricted on the subjective plane, as can be observed in primitive peoples, in infants, and in deaf-mutes who have not been taught words, as well as in pathological defectives such as idiots and some aphasiacs. In mankind as a whole, human nature as we understand it was originally no more than a potential quality and one that, above all, depended for its development on the acquisition of language, a slow, collective, evolutionary process that took centuries; and much the same is true of every individual, who, as it were, serves an apprenticeship to the language—the transmitting agent of cultural influences—of his particular group. However, mankind is not created by language, for language has its origins in that biological peculiarity constituted by man's "larger brain," whose functional potentialities are not realizable by animals, since their brains are insufficiently rich in neurons. It is when the brain is sufficiently mature to encompass language—that is to say, when the child learns to speak—that the quality of being human really asserts itself, as has been shown by studies in the comparative development of children and monkeys. This humanization manifests itself as a social process. An individual is introduced into a society, and finds himself in a relationship with others of his kind: we are only ourselves, and capable of thought, because, as children, and at the appropriate time, our social environment has provided us with the means of thought and therefore with the means of affirming our existence as individuals. Once the appropriate age for acquiring language has been passed, these conditions disappear, and the child who is reared by wolves will learn to speak only with difficulty and will remain capable only of non-human thought. Similarly, the child of primitive savages, although potentially our equal if he acquires our language young enough, will be deprived of all possibility of advancement if there is delay, while the deaf-mute child who is taught the forms of language too late will remain defective in his thought processes. Human thought is a cultural process, and while a man's social environment can be oppressive and can hinder the development of its members, it does not follow that he would be better off without it, that he could develop himself in isolation, for without social contact he would approach the animal state and have only rudimentary thought processes and consciousness. It is this fact that enabled Engels to write, exaggerating slightly,[1] that "the earliest men. . . . were in all essentials

[1] Man is created with an innate cerebral ability for reflection and free will, but these are only developed by cultural influences through the medium of language.

as little free as the animals themselves." As Stalin, who had a sound understanding of the human importance of language, so rightly said: "We speak of thoughts coming into a man's mind before they are expressed in words, suggesting that they exist without the materials of language—naked, so to speak—but this is quite wrong. Whatever thoughts come into a man's mind originate and exist only on the basis of the language's materials, on the basis of its terms and phrases. There are no naked thoughts independent of the language's materials. . . . Thought, as a reality, manifests itself in language, and there is no thought without language." Or, at least, we should add, no truly human thought. Delacroix, in his famous work *Le langage et la pensée,* has exactly formulated the relationship existing between these two elements: "Thought forms language, and in turn is formed by language."

Thus it is important for those who want to understand and classify man to put their trust in language, "this secondary attribute of the human condition that guarantees mankind an infinite destiny in an infinite universe, and that, in its higher aspects, creates knowledge" (Pavlov). So far, linguistics has been the responsibility of several independent groups of specialists who have ignored the common ground lying between them, and there is still far too little liaison between the neurophysiologists and the linguistic experts. A most useful undertaking would be the regrouping of these fields of study—like that which gave birth to cybernetics—that would promote a common effort aiming at a synthesis applied to a better understanding of the human phenomenon.

In this book we shall deal with the psychophysiological aspect of language by explaining the cerebral processes that accomplish it, and by showing how the subject's environmental behavior serves to condition and modify the whole thought process. Certainly there is still much to be discovered in this field, but meanwhile we begin to see more clearly that language is no more than a particular instance of cerebral expression, yet one that has special properties. In this the researches of Pavlov and his pupils on the effects of signals upon reflexes play a considerable role.

In the first part of the book we shall treat of the known facts of animal psychology in comparison with child psychology in order to ascertain precisely how men differ from animals on the plane of language; we shall establish the potentialities and limitation of animal language and we shall examine the various stages in a child's acquisition of speech. In the second part of the book, by describing the cerebral mechanisms and structures responsible for speech, we shall see the resultant effects of verbalization on psychology; and the final section will be devoted to speech deficiencies in man—that is, while not treating the various disorders of speech in any detail, we shall deal successively with those human subjects who have the power of speech but have not learned to talk (such as wolf-reared children) and with those who are cerebrally normal but who are cut off from the human environment by physical deficiency (such as deaf-mutes) and who, to some degree, can give us an idea of how things were with primitive man. Then we shall touch upon pathology by discussing how speech is affected by brain defects and mental disorders, and also we shall examine various types of aphasia and stammering, a study that has made important contributions to the physiology of speech and thought.

By approaching the study of speech in this way we help neurophysiology the better to understand what we are, and what we can become. Man, vainly thinking of his intellect as a mere gift, proud of his technical achievements, seldom congratulates himself on the power of speech, and too often interests himself in it only to deplore its inadequacies—he depreciates speech as mere word-juggling and chit-chat—yet language is the most wonderful of human inventions, and *Homo* is only fully *sapiens* because he is *loquens,* that is, because he has learned to talk. Little has changed in the human body since Paleolithic times, but man's psychology is no longer the same: his intelligence has developed, thanks to language and the perfecting of it. Whereas animals, lacking speech, remain static, man's potentialities are almost limitless and, little by little, the historical process has followed a similar course to biological evolution. Human experience has nothing more astonishing to show than the ability of successive generations to develop speech from a single vocal note that in no way differed at the outset from noises made by animals, and nothing more extraordinary than the process by which speech and thought mutually perfected each other to encompass an awareness of the external world, including man himself, within the confines of the human brain.

What an immense vista of progress lies between man's first simple grunts or squeals—random tracks in the sand at the very start of human history—and the drawings of bison in the caves of Altamira and Lascaux, or, for that matter, between them and the mathematical calculations that can place with precision the universe's most distant galaxies. Every human being seems at birth no better provided for than his primitive ancestors, but with the coming of speech he has at his command the whole accumulation of human knowledge. "With the coming of man," wrote P. Teilhard de Chardin, "a different form of heredity made its appearance and became preponderant, one that had already been tentatively outlined and tried out in the highest forms of insects and vertebrates—that is to say, the heredity of example and education. . . . Heredity, which until then had been essentially a matter of genetics, now became essentially 'noospheric,' " and in a shrinking world, evolving rapidly and inevitably toward the fusion of social groups and the disappearance of the class structure, the same cultural influences will become available to all. However, in comparison with our inborn instinctive reflexes, this induced cultural environment rests on fragile and insecure foundations: after all, a few bees can replenish a hive, but a handful of survivors of "the folly of man" might not be enough to assure the continuance of human civilization.

# *Part One*

# *The Sources of Language*

# 1 / *Animal Language*

In animals, even more than in man, the nervous system—the source of those multiple reactions that constitute behavior—is directly dependent upon the sensory messages it receives. Nerve impulses, originating from sensory perception, act upon the nerve centers to achieve a reflex that is entirely specific and appropriate to the messages that have stimulated it, and the reflex strives to end the stimulus by satisfying the needs provoking it. Some of these reflexes are innate—that is, the animal manifests them from the outset by virtue of the properties of its nervous system and without any conditioning—while others that do not form part of the animal's normal equipment demand an educative process, an apprenticeship made up of the trials and errors of experience, and this is effected either by environment alone or by the active intervention of other individuals, which can be of the same species as the animal or of another species—man, for instance. Moreover, it is sometimes difficult to distinguish between an innate reflex and an acquired one, since certain accomplishments (walking, for example, or flying) that are linked to the maturing of the nervous system can resemble an apprenticeship, and there is also a great deal of interaction between the two types of reflex.

This educative apprenticeship is dependent upon *conditioning,* the process that was studied and elucidated by Pavlov: when a reflex action is induced by a stimulus that coincides with another stimulus—one that by itself would be without any effect—the animal, after a certain number of experiments linking both stimuli, is conditioned to react to the second stimulus as if it were the first, and the ringing of a bell associated with the provision of a meal will eventually induce salivation by itself. In this way the animal, whether in the experimenter's laboratory or in its everyday life, obtains new reflex actions grafted onto its primitive reflexes, innate or acquired, and the messages that release them are termed *signals.* The innumerable and infinitely various messages that reach the animal by way of its senses—emanating both from the outside world and from its own organism—often conflict with each other, but the animal reacts only to those that have a special significance for it or are of vital importance. Moreover, this choice can be made quite automatically, and it does not necessarily involve any awareness at a conscious level. Conditional reflexes exist in the visceral sphere that are never consciously realized (Bykov).

## *Non-Verbal Language*

It is not only during the animal's apprenticeship that it responds to the stimulus of signals. The analysis of sensory messages in connection with the animal's needs is a fundamental attribute of the nervous system that is also met with in the innate reflexes, and it is by reference to it that the modern school of objectivists has explained some of the most curious characteristics of instinctive behavior patterns. An animal at the mercy of its instincts does not judge a situation as a whole, but produces the appropriate reaction in response to a given stimulus—the *evocator* of this reaction—and remains entirely indifferent to all other stimuli although its senses register them perfectly. Instinctive behavior is achieved by a succession of reflexes arranged in series, each of which is released by a different evocator, one that is active only at the desired moment of the cycle, and the animal is no more responsible for the correct functioning of its instinct than it is for the structural harmony of its organism. Indeed, it is usually incapable of adjusting errors produced by disturbances in the normal unfolding of the series, and a reaction designed to take place at a particular stage in normal circumstances will continue to take place even if conditions are changed artificially.

This is not the place to go into these phenomena in any detail, and it is enough for us to know that the nervous system's constitution makes it apt to react to significant messages in a way that can be either innate or acquired, its sensitivity to different signals varying according to the state of the nerve centers that insure a relationship between the reflex and the animal's needs: it is the signal alone that is effective. Thus a hunting wasp preying on bees at first reacts only to objects met with in flight and shows nothing if a bee is placed beside it, and when the prey has been seen, the wasp is guided entirely by scent and only attacks if the scent indicates a bee, whereupon tactile stimuli will provoke it to extrude its sting. Since animals lack conscious control of their reactions, it is easy to deceive them with decoys that act as evocators, and thus a male butterfly will attempt to copulate with a piece of paper impregnated with the female's scent while remaining indifferent to the sight of a female that has been deprived of scent. The male robin's aggressive instincts are released by the sight of his congener's red plumage, and he will attack the detached feathers while ignoring the bird from which they were plucked. The animal world is a world of signs, and among them there are many that establish the relationships existing between individuals, whether they are of different species (hunter and hunted) or of the same species (male and female, parents and young, or individuals of the same sex such as male rivals during the mating season, etc.). It will be seen that some apparently insignificant details—various markings, for instance, such as the robin's red breast—whose import formerly confounded the anthropomorphically inclined observer have, in fact, considerable importance as far as the species' life cycle is concerned. The baby gulls that offer their beaks to their mother for food do so only as a result of the stimulus that her beak's coloration presents, and it is possible for a stimulus signal to be ambiguous if its significance depends upon its context—for instance, an egg in the nest is something to be incubated; an egg anywhere else is something to be eaten; while an egg that rolls from the nest releases two opposing behavior reflexes, and the bird hesitates. Sexual relationships depend upon several different types of evocator: butterflies are attracted by scent, glowworms by light, while the mating displays of birds bring into play visual evocators, and particular postures and movements are essential to bring the female into a state of receptivity.

Thus there are numerous means of communication in the animal world that compensate for the absence of speech. Moreover we find comparable means of communication in our own species when *gestures* are sufficiently significant to convey the idea of certain simple needs to those whose language we cannot speak, and gesture language attains an even greater importance among primitive peoples. It is interesting to note similarities between certain primitive dances and the mating displays of birds, and this is observable quite apart from any geographical propinquity.

A distinction must be made between evocators expressed involuntarily by an individual and those that are the result of a behavior reflex, such as a display of pigmentation or the execution of a mating display. Those that have a genuine informative value quite apart from their reflex-inducing powers—thus achieving a true equivalent of speech—are rather few.

## *The Dance Language of Bees*

Such a role—that is, communication—is especially achieved by two types of signal, one of these being the bees' informative dances, discovered by von Frisch, and another the sounds made by insects and vertebrates, especially by birds and mammals. These latter form a genuine homologue of human language, although in fact it must be considered simply as an auditory evocator.

The communal work carried out by social insects postulates the existence of a means of communication, yet so far we know little of the methods employed by termites, for instance, to achieve remarkable coordination in the building of their complex constructions.

On the other hand, von Frisch's meticulous observations have enabled him to establish that one bee can inform another of the whereabouts of food by telling it that a particular species of flower will be found in a particular direction and at such-and-such a distance, these last two details being conveyed by a sort of *dance language.* The bee goes through a dance routine that has the form of a figure eight, and that is inclined to the perpendicular to a greater or lesser degree. The speed of the dance—that is, the number of circuits flown per second—is in inverse ratio to the distance that is being communicated, and this can be anything from a hundred yards up to four miles, while shorter distances are indicated by a different kind of dance. The direction of the food supply is conveyed by the dance routine's angle of inclination, which is equal to the angle formed by two imaginary lines converging upon the hive from the food supply and from the sun. The bee's eye is sensitive to the polarization of light, and so it can tell the direction of the sun even when it is obscured by clouds, and when the food supply is on the far side of a hill the bee states its direction in the usual way, but in conveying its distance takes the hill's contours into consideration. The exactness of the information communicated is proved by the fact that, although the bee that discovers the food supply does not return to it, its comrades find their way straight to it without difficulty, and, indeed, human observers have themselves succeeded in learning the dance language, and so can discover what is conveyed by the bee.

We have no finer example than this of non-auditory communication in animals, yet here again a behavior pattern was lightly passed over unremarked for a long time, while unscientific observers simply concluded that the bee was showing its joy at getting back to the hive, an entirely unacceptable anthropomorphism. Even the scientific observer attached no special importance to this manifestation of excitement in the first instance; the truth is that the bee's behavior makes sense only to the bee.

## *Animal Noises and Bird Song*

A genuine language by means of acoustic signals is found among numerous insects that are equipped with stridulant organs specially designed to emit shrill sounds, and even ultrasonic sounds to which their auditory systems are sensitive.[1] Whereas with butterflies it is the male that is attracted to the female by her scent, among grasshoppers it is the female that is attracted by the male's stridulation. Modern methods of recording and analyzing sound enable insect noises to be studied like voices; there are several different types of sound corresponding to various different functions—sounds that imply warning, calling, courtship, etc., and in France these have been thoroughly studied by Busnel and his colleagues.

Animals can be artificially attracted by sound signals, and the female will make for the loudspeaker that transmits the male's noise to her. Sound attraction among insects lacks specificity, and various noises quite different from the normal mating call can agitate the female by *phonotropism.* In some species where there is an exchange of sounds between the sexes, communication can be established with an insect by an experimenter calling to it, and this will lead the insect right up to the experimenter's mouth; by an extension of this technique it is possible that one day we shall be able to control the movements of locust swarms. Before that can happen more research will be necessary to establish exactly what proportion of these reactions to sound signals is due simply to the releasing of an elementary behavior pattern on the basis of certain tropisms, and what proportion really has an informative value arguing a higher psychological level.

This is the level attained by the higher vertebrates,

[1] Numerous aquatic animals emit sounds that interfere with submarine detection and that can explode acoustic mines.

in which vocal sounds produced by an organ analogous to the human larynx[2] and caught by a true ear, highly sensitive to frequencies, are collected by a complex brain. Uttered sounds play a considerable role in the life of various species, but information transmitted in this way is always very rudimentary and of the same order as that conveyed by other types of signal. Thus the animal uses sound to advertise its presence, scaring intruders from its territory without having to resort to violence, or to call its mate. But its territory can also be indicated with the help of olfactory signals provided by urine or the products of special glands, and particular physical postures are also highly significant.

Careful analysis reveals that different animal cries indicate various different things; the howler monkeys have at their command fifteen to twenty different cries, by means of which they can convey alarm, command, uneasiness and enjoyment; then there are the wailing uttered by the female calling to her lost offspring, the young one's cry for help, and the particular sound it makes when it wants to be fondled. Chimpanzees have no fewer than thirty-two sounds, and hens can relate ten different cries to different situations. As Armstrong has written, the "frequent vocal utterances, more or less melodious, some loud and some subdued, together with song, are only a plentiful type of signal, more auditory than visual, by which a bird influences its fellows. From the functional point of view, it is not possible to establish the exact distinction between songs and cries." The

[2] Birds usually have a *syrinx,* which is comparable to a larynx, but is placed lower down at the bronchial bifurcation.

reasons "why birds sing" are legion: a bird sings to identify itself to another of the same species, to indicate its whereabouts and its territory, to establish its vigor and authority (its social rank, for instance), to make known its sexual status or the whereabouts of the nest, to attract the female, to intimidate a rival, to synchronize its sexual cycle with that of its mate, to announce a change of activity, or to coax the young ones out of the nest.

In contrast to human speech, which is *learned,* animal language is for the most part *innate,* as are the cries of a newborn baby, and—to take the case of monkeys born in captivity—the young ones utter sounds appropriate to their species as soon as they reach the right age and understand the cries of their congeners. Certain birds must be excluded from this generalization, especially the fine songsters among the Passeriformes, who must learn to sing. Some nightingales are better songsters than others, and during the course of their life their gift for singing can show improvement. Indeed, it is not hereditary: the young ones have to be taught to sing, and veritable singing classes are organized for them. Canary-trainers place the young birds near expert songsters; a young bird in contact with adult birds of a different species will learn to sing their song rather than instinctively singing that of its own species, but its song will show specific characteristics, and as soon as it hears the song of its own species it will choose it for preference. Contact with a fine songster may have a considerable effect on a young bird, even before it has reached the age for singing.

This aptitude of birds for learning a language is also

found in other species, in particular among parrots, which have a remarkable gift for imitating the human voice. This bird possesses vocal organs that lend themselves to articulated speech, but above all it has the gift of imitation, which, contrary to popular opinion, is just what monkeys are most lacking in. That parrots are among the more intelligent birds can be shown by the weight of their brains, and they are often aware of the correct use of such human speech as they are taught, but this is due to ordinary conditioned reflexes responding to a signal and not to any real mastery of the language. Without crediting everything that is said on the subject, it is certain that parrots often know quite well how to use their talent for their own ends, but in this they are no different from all other trained animals, which often astonish by their understanding of the spoken word. Sometimes parrots show themselves capable of inventing new words, and, as H. Roger tells us, "parrots, understanding the sense of certain words and phrases, know how to say the right things to cause amusement, or they can arouse their audience's compassion with sighs and groans. Like children, they seize on the significance of certain groups of words, but soon an important difference shows itself. The child will presently learn to separate the various words of a phrase and to join them up to others, but this is something the bird cannot do. With humans the words become mobile, but with birds they remain forever static and united."

Such are the highest possibilities of animal language. With animals, signals by means of sound never acquire the importance reserved for human speech, but if the latter had not had its origins in manifestations of this sort, as we shall see, the vocal phenomena of animals would not be worth describing except as examples of communication by signals. The only difference between the higher and lower species resides in the consciousness with which these vocal signals are employed, in the mastery attained over them, and in an awareness of the possibilities of adapting them to a life growing more and more complex. Simple performance, effected automatically and passively by means of reflexes and tropisms, has to be succeeded by an intelligent grasp of given situations as well as by some degree of control over the instincts, and although among animals language already serves the intelligence, it can contribute only feebly to its improvement, since animal intelligence, inhibited by a nervous system of limited scope, cannot be raised much above an elementary level, and its processes are of the same order, but less developed, as human thought carried on by means of non-verbal images.

## 2 / *From Animal to Man*

"It is difficult," says Chauvin, "to define whether the differences between animal language and human speech are differences of degree or of kind, but frame the question in another way and it becomes easier to answer: is there nothing in animal language that recalls human speech? As we have seen, it is difficult to answer this question negatively. However, if the difference is only one of degree, I think it is always so great as to produce a radical division between animals and man."

On the zoological plane there is no fundamental difference between man and animals, and man differs from the anthropoid apes in only a few anatomical details. Morphologically his brain is not very different, but—and it is in this that the fundamental dissimilarity lies—it is much larger, which is to say that it contains many more neurons, and this in turn implies infinitely greater functional potentialities since all cerebral operation relies upon the neurons' shifting associations. Roughly speaking, the human brain has four times more neurons than that of the anthropoids, and twice as many as that of the *Pithecanthropus,* the intermediary fossil species. Language, and all other psychological manifestations, depend upon just that difference which is responsible for a better nervous control of the vocal organs(and one that is voluntary), better auditory perception, better coordination between the auditory tract and the motor system, infinitely greater aptitude for memory, and thus for educability and the development of conditioned reflexes, and indeed, a firmer grasp of consciousness as a whole.

The greater contains the lesser, and thus man, infinitely the superior on the plane of language, is able to utter sound signals analogous to those used in animal language, and to some extent he is able to understand animals—at least those nearest to him—and to be understood by them. From this animal language man, capable of progress and invention, has developed a new, purely human language, with which he can convey the very essence as well as the meaning of his thought, and this allows him to leave the animal level far behind. Animals are quite incapable of acquiring human speech (excepting the mimicry of parrots), and training only enables them to understand it to a very superficial degree. In any case, the animal is unable to make any notable intellectual progress by means of human speech, and for him it is never more than another variety of animal language.

## *Animal Language in Man*

When we are in a foreign country whose language we do not understand we are unable to exchange ideas, for which speech is necessary. We know quite well how to convey our basic needs and sentiments by resorting to gestures, mime and sounds that constitute a universal language not far removed from animal language; and similarly, when we are at the mercy of a violent emotion there is no need of words to show our joy, our pain or our anguish. In everyday speech certain basic interjections serve as calls or as refusals, and certain imitations of noises have attached themselves to this mode of expression.[1] Cries, mimicry and gesture are the child's first language, and they are also the means of expression of the deaf-mute. They constitute a system of communication that allows the higher animals—mammals and birds, especially when they have been domesticated, for, as Saint-Exupéry said, to domesticate is to contract a relationship—to understand us and to make themselves understood by us, such understanding remaining at their level, that is to say, on the plane of desires and feelings; and this sort of relationship with man is even greater where monkeys are concerned. Comparable behavior on the part of even lower creatures has frequently led unscientific observation toward an inadmissible anthropomorphism, but, without attaching our ab-

[1] Ordinary speech, apart from its semantic role (informing by means of the intellect), has also an aesthetic role, in that it conveys information by means of its tone, and this has been studied recently by A. Moles.

stract conceptions to animals, Lapicque considers that it is possible for at least the higher vertebrates to assimilate elementary reactions. The study of animal psychology is a behavioristic science that recognizes this common ground between animals and man in endeavoring to decipher all the signs of the animal world—signs whose significance escapes us, either because our senses are inadequate or because we are not attuned to notice things that are not human concerns, or analogous to them. The savage, whose vital preoccupations and natural environment are nearer to those of the animal, remains closer to it in all ways; in order to attract the animal and catch it with ease, he knows how to imitate it almost perfectly. If man, by means of training, can develop an animal's educational potentialities to the maximum until it performs feats that greatly exceed the attainments of its native state—feats of which even the most spectacular have not the value of intelligence tests put to the animal by experimentation—the opposite is also true, and the animal can dehumanize man: children reared by wolves are incapable of human speech, but become completely integrated in the wolves' society whose habits they have acquired. Here dehumanization goes far deeper than the humanization of animals ever goes, since the latter always remains very superficial.

## *Characteristics of Human Speech*

What distinguishes human speech, produced under the control of the largest brain among animals, lies for a start in the executive sphere, or, to be exact, in the pharyngo-buccal area surmounting the larynx, since it is by modifications of the form of this area that an extremely wide range of sounds *(phonemes)* is produced, thereby insuring an *articulated* language. The power of uttering these sounds is innate in man and, by an extension of this power, he rings the changes on the various sounds at his command to create a language made up of words, thereby evolving for himself a highly complicated vocal instrument, and one that is always in the process of improvement; thus he is no longer limited in the way that all animals are limited, if we except those birds that, as we have seen, can manage a little in the way of articulation. For another thing, man is richly endowed with the ability to imitate spoken sounds—as are some birds, although in a lesser degree—and thus he can learn to reproduce words he has heard spoken and he will absorb those social sound codes that, having their roots in the distant past, are the various languages. Man is essentially a social being, living in a complex environment that he seeks to understand and to modify according to his requirements and, badly served by his diminished instincts, he experiences a need for an ever-better means of communication, and this is the motivation that impels him to perfect his language. Above all, however—and it is here that a revolution has been brought about by human speech—this infinite potentiality involves more than the verbal grasp of just a few signals indicating simple situations and feelings: to borrow Haldane's expression, language inclines to become *descriptive,* it becomes an instrument of symbolism, everything tends to be given a name and there is a tendency for the objects of the exterior world to be designated by a sound symbol[2] that permits them to be easily evoked even in their absence. The word becomes detached from the object and acquires an independent life. From then on language is no longer essentially a means of communication, a series of signals between two individuals, external to the individual who utters it and for whom it has no value, but becomes an *instrument of thought*. Only man makes use in that way of an *internal language,* which is no longer speech, since it is not expressed in sound, but which is nothing less than the transposition of a sound message to the cerebral plane. Simple animal thought, making use of the visual images of objects, is replaced by an association of verbal images that allows an enormous expansion of thought and of self-awareness.

Thus man, by making use of the possibilities of articulated language to describe objects, is provided with a means of thought, and a means by which the external signal can be transferred to the mind—a transition from the concrete to the abstract. Every man living normally in a society has the ability to create for himself a personal language, and this ability sometimes shows itself in children and in certain mental patients, not to speak of slang and jargon used by exclusive coteries, but usually man is content to learn the language of his ethnic group, rich in cultural acquisitions from the past, and by learning a ready-made language in these conditions he acquires an instrument of thought and

[2] In fact, the symbol goes beyond the language, and it is better to think of language as a higher order of signal (Pavlov).

does not need to create one by creating a language. The point we want to make is that man lacking human social contact does not learn to talk, and this is shown by all examples in which human subjects have been deprived of hearing the human voice from earliest infancy. Deaf-mutes, ignorant of speech, attempt to replace it by gesture language, but since the latter's lack of precision renders it inferior as a means of symbolization, it lends itself badly to the establishing of human thought. It is when man creates human thought for himself by virtue of an internal language that he learns to give his gestures enough precision to enable him to express this thought, and this is exemplified by writing, mankind's secondary language, which is composed of gestures and whose acquisition by humanity has been a much slower process: writing is allied to verbal symbolization only secondarily, since it is produced by representative outlines and the sound does not survive the inscription.

Thus human thought shows itself as originating from the need of a social species with a developed brain for a means of communication; humanity, by wanting to act and transform the world communally, has transformed itself, and the progress of civilization has always been a conjoint progress of language and thought, and action. It should be remarked, moreover, that even among the social species of insects, which are richer in innate instinct than in acquired intelligence, the higher forms of thought activity manifest themselves, particularly language such as the extraordinary danced language of the bees, which equally relates to the common effort. As Haldane points out, when a child says to his mother "I'm hungry" or "I want to go to sleep" he is still animal, but when he says "This is what I did this morning" he begins to be human.

## *Animals and Human Speech*

When man voluntarily renounces speech in order to make himself understood by an animal—using quasi-animal means to express what he feels—he nonetheless remains human from the point of view of his thoughts: there is no equality between man and animal when it comes to conversation by gestures. Animal thought, even if it has in effect the same content as human thought, is fundamentally different in its internal aspect and only with difficulty is it possible for us to represent our thought in a non-verbal form. Can the animal that we train, that we domesticate by giving it certain desires and requirements, that we humanize by confronting it with human problems—can this animal attain speech? Some painstaking experiments have been carried out on young apes, notably on chimpanzees and orangutans, with the idea of teaching them to speak. By themselves, unlike human children, they make no attempt to imitate the human voice, while efforts to train them to this with rewards and encouragement have usually been in vain, and the most that they have managed after a great deal of delay has been the reproduction of some human sounds and, in exceptional instances, the pronouncing of such simple words as "papa" and "cup," which words are thereafter used correctly and to good purpose. Nevertheless monkeys have well-developed larynxes with apparently everything that is needed for speech. What monkeys lack is, first, a brain sufficiently developed to achieve the complex control of the pharyngobuccal muscles necessary for articulation and secondly, enough intelligence to understand the symbolism of language, while parrots, better provided as regards articulation and imitation than monkeys, are even less intelligent. A parrot with a monkey's brain might prove forthcoming. Animal intelligence, which in monkeys can go so far as to achieve the making and using of quite elaborate tools, is incapable of grasping the real significance of human language. Animals, badly equipped for speech, seem much better at understanding, and there are numerous spoken words that will operate conditioned reflexes: Kohts's chimpanzee understood twenty-four different phrases, and dogs can recognize a word in a phrase even when it is not ostensibly addressed to them. Yet interesting though these facts are, they do not go beyond the level of animal intelligence and animal language. By simple training—that is, conditioning—the animal learns to attach a particular significance to a particular sound signal, which, however, always remains external to it. It is a notification that does not integrate with the animal's thought processes and therefore does not become a symbol independent of reality. It is no more than an animal's understanding of a human sound and animal thoughts cannot be put into words.

Yet if the higher apes have little aptitude as regards language, they are nevertheless capable of some understanding of the use of symbols, and chimpanzees have been trained to use coins to operate a slot machine dispensing food, to distinguish genuine coins from counterfeit, to hoard their coins with a view to the future, and to make change. They understand the practical value of them, but how far does this understanding go, and is it not simply a matter of some impressive training, teaching them to use a special tool, yet one that perhaps demands less intelligence than the joining together of two pieces of bamboo to make a long stick? Might not a white rat be trained to exchange a coin for food? As regards animal psychology, it is advisable to be very wary in all ways. Language remains the barrier that radically divides animals from man, and, to the extent that an animal understands human language, it is not an instrument of thought, but a simple signal, and therefore an animal language. The capability of human speech is an attribute of the human brain, and therefore the possibility of it has characterized the human species from the beginning. Modern theories of evolution argue in favor of a sudden appearance of the various species by a mutation, and it seems that from the outset man, although not speaking, has been potentially able to speak. Paleontology, however, has discovered the existence of creatures, *Pithecanthropus* and *Sinanthropus,* with a brain intermediary between that of the anthropoid apes and that of man, so what language had they? Alas, only the writers of science fiction would venture to tell us! We cannot obtain any idea of the physiology of language by studying the anatomy of the brain, since the centers are analogous, the numbers of the neurons being the only difference, and we do not know the minimum quantity of neurons necessary for speech to become possible. It is certainly highly probable that language was able to exist at the intermediary stage between monkeys and man. The degree of educability is the only test that can determine whether the lack of language is due to an inherently weak potentiality for language, or to a linguistically inferior cultural level. The only thing that can be said for certain is that all present-day so-called savages, no matter how primitive their language, can acquire our cultural standards if their education is taken in hand before the age of five. It is possible for a civilized person to learn a language at any age if, as a child, he has had an education linguistically sufficient to provide him with an evolved thought process, and, on the other hand, a child who has not been equipped with such a thought process within the necessary time can never acquire it thereafter: the brain has lost the opportunity. The adult's thought process is entirely dependent upon the language he has learned as a child. Without going into the question of wolf-reared children, who, deprived of language, are virtually incapable of acquiring it after a certain age, it is certain that in our own society even the differences in speech due to educational inequalities between the classes constitute an obstacle extremely difficult to surmount, as was so rightly shown by Van der Meersch in *The Poor Girl,* or by Giono, when he compares the language of a peasant from the Basses-Alpes with that of a magistrate. We have an inalienable duty to provide every child—even the mentally deficient—with the maximum education in linguistics, so that it can realize the sum total of its human potentialities, and this duty is utterly overlooked by our unjust society, dedicated as it is to establishing completely unnatural inequalities between men and persisting as it does in making of culture—language in its highest form—a privilege reserved for the rich.

# 3 / *The Acquisition of Language*

It is not possible for us to retrace further back than the historical period the slow steps by which humanity, capable of articulated sounds from the outset, acceded to the symbolic qualities of language. When the study of linguistics attempts to discover the origins of the great families into which present-day languages are classified it can do no more than go back into the relatively recent past, and that only with difficulty—that is, the recent past in comparison with the half-million years that have elapsed since the human species and its immediate forerunners first started their cultural adventure on dry land, with infinitely slow progress in the first place, but progress that speeded up as time went on in accordance with the law that informs the whole evolutionary process. Present-day primitive peoples, who are backward and sometimes degenerate, go a long way toward being faithful witnesses of humanity's beginnings.

But one may begin with any man: psychological studies comparing monkeys and children show that before the acquisition of language there is an incontestable relationship between their respective intelligences. Etymologically the word "infant" means one who cannot speak, and each infant, by exploiting his developing neuromotor control, should be able to acquire the language furnished by those about him. By learning to speak he learns to think, and then his nebulous consciousness can blossom into a true human consciousness. Nowadays numerous studies enable us to examine and decipher the various stages in the learning of language. A progressive evolution leads insensibly from the child's birth cries to constructed speech, which takes shape in the course of the third year, and this process continues, slowly and gradually, during the years that follow,[1] all education, all development of the power of reasoning and abstraction being no more than the perfecting of language, to which writing is presently added. The sensorimotor process develops along the following lines: first the child becomes capable of recognizing the sounds it hears; then it must gain control over the complex assembly of muscular reactions that permit the utterance of the desired sounds. Later, writing imposes the same problems in the visual sphere (reading), as well as demanding accurate motor control of the hand. Thus it is not surprising that progress in the acquisition of language should be linked to sensitivomotor development.

[1] A child who becomes deaf before the age of six or seven will forget as much speech as he has learned trough still having insufficient mastery of it.

## *Maturation and Apprenticeship*

Various birds and mammals come into the world sufficiently developed to be able to lead a fairly active life from the outset, but man's offspring, like that of monkeys, is born in a highly incomplete state: although the visceral system is complete, and although the larynx and organs of respiration are ready for use a long time before air-breathing is possible, the brain, by contrast, is thoroughly behindhand: early on it will have attained its fundamental structures and its cellular neuronic equipment, all of which will serve it throughout life, but its connective tissues and its myelinic differentiations, which insure normal functioning, are completed only slowly, and the brain is not completely formed until the child reaches the age of seven.[2] Development during the first few years—and especially the startling progress made during the very first year—depends upon this progressive *maturation* of the brain, which, upon the organism's acquisition of sensorimotor mastery, insures the first development of consciousness. Subsequently, with the brain fully formed as regards structure, and permitting reflective thought, the child, and then the adolescent, will learn to make ever-better use of it until, with the appearance at puberty of sexuality, maturity is reached and the subject is in full possession of all its physical attributes, these changes reacting also upon the brain's functioning. Man and monkey, once they have escaped from the silence of prenatal life, mature their brains in a social environment,

[2] Much sooner in monkeys, which become adult more quickly.

but in the monkey's case, its social environment being somewhat restricted, the maturation takes place rapidly and maturity of the nervous system coincides with the appearance of sexuality and the achievement of the adult state: the nervous development permits the appearance of inborn instinctive behavior patterns at their appointed time, and there is little room for the acquisition of education or the development of the intelligence. On the other hand, man, whose instincts are restricted, experiences manifestations of education and of intelligence even before his brain is fully developed, and this is principally due to the acquisition of language, which makes him fully a human being, that is, capable of infinite progress. Yet, having acquired this tool, he is still a child, spared an adult's cares, and the long periods that separate his learning to talk from puberty, then puberty from the adult state—two stages that do not exist in the monkey's growth pattern—enable him to realize his possibilities, unless dehumanizing social injustices hinder the process. Thus basically equipped during the course of his long infancy, the adult man becomes capable of endless progress, something denied to the savage and the uneducated, who have not learned to use their brains culturally; and even more forcibly is it denied to the monkey, who, in a natural state, has little need of initiative, and whose intellectual attainments in contact with man, although remarkable, are only very rudimentary.

Yet even though man had a larger brain from the beginning and one richer in potential than in innate preestablished mechanisms, the other biological innovations that encouraged its growth and favored its activity must not be forgotten; these are the prolongation of the period of growth and the acquisition of an upright posture, the latter being essential for humanization since it frees the hands and allows a considerable expansion of the cranium by altering the position of the head, while frontal and facial developments add scope for articulation to the larynx, something not easily compatible with an animal's muzzle.

Two factors have parts to play in the development of an organism—the first is the organism's own dynamism released by an outburst of vitality coincident with the realization of an individual from the time of fertilization, and the second devolves from the influence of the organism's environment. It is rightly maintained that new acquisitions resulting from the first of these factors, which insures that each function comes into play at the right time, simply constitute a spontaneous maturation of the nervous system and not an apprenticeship; this is true as regards mastery of the motor controls, for instance, in walking, or in the beginnings of articulated speech. The child walks, not because he is taught to, but because the maturation of his nervous system makes walking possible, and some experiments in which lessons in walking have been withheld have clearly shown that they are not indispensable; and in the same way, a deaf baby will utter sounds. The most drastic mutilations carried out in experimental embryology are often unable to prevent the nervous system from realizing itself. However, very soon the second factor intervenes and the environment, by providing important motives for using the function, contributes to the perfecting of it: the child becomes interested in walking and talking, and in this those about him participate. Thus his personal efforts are added to his innate and spontaneous inclination to walk and talk, and in this way maturation is encouraged. Conversely, lack of use acts in the opposite way: the monkey, whose pupils are occluded at birth, becomes inept at seeing, and the deaf child presently ceases to utter sounds. If the messages of the senses are not indispensable to nervous growth and maturation, their assistance is essential for maintaining the faculties. However, environment does more than merely collaborate with the organism's dynamism; above all, to those reactions that are built into the nervous structure by heredity—the nervous mechanism's automatic functions—it adds the possibility of new reactions by the operation of conditioned reflexes, and, for cerebral functioning, this is the fundamental means of progress. The child learns certain behavior patterns, gestures and language adapted to circumstances and to certain external signals. It becomes extremely difficult to distinguish between what is innate and what is learned, since not only do innate attributes simulate acquired characteristics, but the process of apprenticeship tends to develop and perfect all the hereditary qualities; every motor activity of the adult depends upon conditioning. For man, it is essential that the maturation of his brain takes place in a social environment, so that while the possibilities of his organism are realizing themselves, they are immediately surrounded by a climate of educative development that will otherwise become harder and harder to acquire. A child of seven still seems a long way from the adult state, yet it has nevertheless already undergone irreversible educative influences: as we have said, if one wants a primitive child to adapt himself fully to our civilization, he must be taken in hand before the age of five. The hereditary differences between men of different ethnic groups are weak and affect only matters of detail, but what does separate them are the acquisitions of earliest childhood, since, as they have learned to talk, so have they learned to think; psychiatry has reached the same conclusions as regards character and the emotions.

## *The Stages of Speech Acquisition*

Let us examine briefly, and from the point of view of language, the way in which a child, by living and playing during the course of his first few years, accomplishes the prodigious educative task by which he learns to make use of the potentialities offered him by the spontaneous growth of his brain, for the purpose of achieving his desires and requirements and adapting himself better and better to the world about him, progressing from a vegetative state at birth to the glories of walking and talking that enable him to confront the world with a distinct and personal identity.

The newborn baby, with his cerebral cortex still unable to function, first manifests his presence by *cries* that convey, at one and the same time, the fact of his vitality, the onset of respiratory and laryngal functioning, and the first reflex symptoms of a certain amount of discomfort due to the change of environment and the difficulties of being born. As the baby adapts himself to his new environment and his needs are attended to, his cries, released by reflexes in the brain's lower centers, die down. Premature births show that the ability to cry is acquired some time before the foetus is fully developed.

For some weeks the child, deep in an almost continuous sleep, leads a vegetative life, in which his maturation proceeds actively, and at that time he is nearly without contact with the world. His cries are related to such matters as an obscure feeling of discomfort, desire for food, digestive troubles, the need to be changed, occasionally by serious pain, or by sudden changes inducing elementary fear. These cries are spontaneous and without purpose, but the reactions they produce in those looking after the child lead to the satisfaction of its needs, and the cries stop. Very soon an elementary educative factor manifests itself, and the cry becomes a call of the same order as animal language, but with a degree of consciousness less than in one of the higher animals: the child who cries because he needs something cries in order to put an end to this state of need, and he becomes more and more conscious of the usefulness of his cries. Then, as his need for sleep grows less, he cries to be taken up, thereby affirming his instincts toward sociability. The cries differ to some extent, permitting distinction between various types of elementary emotion, and when the baby is a month old he can show pleasure by means of a particular cry. The smile, which is at first a simple reflex, becomes imitative between two and three months, then spontaneous, and finds its full expression as laughter at six to eight months. Tears make their debut at six weeks to two months, but it is not until four to six months that they express unhappiness. The child can achieve a convincing expression of vexation at two to three months.

The *pre-linguistic* period opened by cries is completed after some eight weeks by babbling sounds *(lallation),* a sort of vocal play that persists until the child is a year old; this is similar to the bird stage of language. This is the first manifestation of articular activity, that is, of buccopharyngal modulation of the voice. What happens is that an innate process enables the brain's higher centers to coordinate the articulating muscles, and since this does not depend upon environment it appears even in deaf babies: thus the human child becomes adept at articulated language, and he exercises his newly acquired mastery because the sounds give him pleasure when he hears himself, or, if deaf, because he feels the movements of his phonatory organs. These spontaneous babblings, whose only purpose is to encourage growth and maturation, increasingly insure the possibility of the child's achieving real sounds, that is, the phonemes necessary for adult speech, and help him to approach the stage at which all human sounds are possible; so far, however, he is not influenced by the speech of those in charge of him.

This stage of lallation is imperceptibly overtaken by a *pre-verbal* stage as the child's interest is aroused by his spontaneous and innate reactions; this phase is only slightly in evidence in the deaf child, who presently becomes mute, since the sensations of laryngal movement and the sight of his parents' lips moving are not enough to make him persist in vocalization, which now stops. The normal child hears himself, and in the course of play creates a whole cycle of audiophonatory conditioning: he no longer babbles at random, but teaches himself to repeat the sounds he utters, and he will tend, for example, to repeat the same sound twice, achieving modest and quite meaningless "pe-pe" or "mm-mm" noises, in which his ecstatic entourage believe that they can already detect his first words. Moreover, while his cries were entirely his own, he recognizes that the sounds he produces in this pre-verbal stage have something in common with the speech of his entourage—this entourage that he finds so interesting, since it attends to his needs—and, by grouping the phonemes, he attempts to reproduce what he hears, especially the rhythms and cadences of adult speech, and the more he does so, the more will his fascinated entourage tirelessly suggest simple sounds for him to imitate. However, the child does not always imitate the sounds obediently and immediately, but makes spontaneous use of as much as he has registered.

So far, it has been only the child's cries that have had any value for him as a sound message, but now, little by little—and this is the start of the *linguistic period*—he comes to *understand* that the speech of his entourage has a significance; certain sounds, the cadences of certain simple phrases, then certain actual words recurring constantly in the same context, begin to acquire meaning, and this period of understanding first shows itself somewhat indefinitely at about the third month, and continues to develop until the seventh to ninth month, varying considerably with the individual. For some time none of this shows itself in the child's subjective behavior. Then a stage of higher imitation is reached, and now it is no longer merely sounds that are imitated, but words, and it has become the child's aim to speak and to provide itself with speech in place of cries as a means of communication.

Speaking the language lags behind the understanding of it. Throughout the period that Pichon calls the *locutory* phase—from about the tenth month to the twentieth—the child learns to understand and use the adult's language better and better, making himself understood in it with increasing facility until in the course of his second year he discovers that "all objects can be named, and that everything can be said." At first he utters only interjections and isolated words, pronunciation is imperfect and so far there are no phrases indicative of an internal language of concepts and judgments. Little by little he increases his vocabulary, and its rate of growth reaches its maximum between sixteen and twenty-two months. The child tends to give each word a limited sense until, by a process of trial and error, he finally arrives at its exact meaning. The first, often fortuitous word, spoken at about one year, has no great importance in relation to the evolutionary process as a whole, and more important is the association of two words in an attempt at a phrase, something that is much delayed in the feeble-minded. Normally this joining of two words occurs at about twenty-two months, but before this stage is reached a single word will be used to say more than itself, and then it is the equivalent of a phrase.

Thus, between twenty months and two-and-a-half years, the child is in possession of a genuine elementary language, a sort of jargon with rudimentary phrases, already enabling him to express himself: he can pass opinions in pidgin phrases and make use of pronouns,[3] but he refers to himself in the third person, and the stage preceding true speech is marked by the appearance of the pronouns "I," "me" and "myself" at two-and-a-half years. Thus less than two years have sufficed to progress from lallation to language, from meaningless articular play to the symbolism of words, and from isolated sounds to elementary syntactic relationships. Nevertheless a great deal of progress is still needed before the tool is forged, and before the arrival of human thought, which is concerned not with images but with words. Essentially it is in the course of the second and third years that, thanks to the acquisition of speech, the transition is made from the animal state to the human state as regards the thought process, and when the child starts to refer to himself as "I" he has acquired total psychological consciousness of his ego. By understanding, and then speaking the language, he learns not only to express himself and to make himself understood, but also to realize the possibilities of thought, and thus he becomes subjectively aware of the world and of himself in relation to it. It will be seen how irrational it is for adults to disturb this development by speaking to children in baby language, which can

[3] The syntactic organization of the phrase is related to the progress made in distinguishing the self from the external world.

only retard their acquisition of genuine thought. The incapacity of a child who does not yet know how to speak properly is more than faulty expression on the part of an intelligence still inept at expressing itself. It reflects an actual intellectual incapacity—the functioning of the brain is still confused—it betrays thought processes that are still unformed and deficient, and they will remain like that unless they stimulate themselves into constructing an internal language. Mastery of language is not concerned only with expressing oneself to others (what Piaget calls "socialized language"), but also in expressing oneself to oneself: language termed *egocentric,* in which the child speaks to himself for his own edification, is especially important when the child is younger and it can go as far as the creation of new words, or even of a special language.[4]

## *Speech and Intelligence*

The exclusive importance of speech in the humanization of the thought process is proved not only by the example of men deprived of speech—and we will return to them presently—but by studies in objective psychology consisting of some exact tests of non-verbalized practical intelligence in which the attainments of monkeys are compared with those of children. Particularly important

[4] In later years the child who knows how to speak will learn to analyze his speech (grammar), and to apply orthography by separating the letters composing words (spelling), and only in this way will he gain full and free mastery of the language.

are the studies commenced in France by Boutan, and developed notably by the Kellogs and N. Kohts, in which young monkeys and young children were compared. They led to the general conclusion that, for a start, monkey and child have an intelligence of the same order at comparable ages, the monkey often having some advantage, notably as regards dexterity and skill: intelligence tests involving short cuts and detours, the use of tools, the releasing of mechanisms (in box puzzles especially), etc., did not show any difference between them.[5] During the last quarter of the first year it can be said that the child is at the chimpanzee stage. Then a moment comes in which everything changes, in which the child starts to make giant strides, solving problems that invariably elude the monkey. It has been proved that this happens when the child reaches the age of speech, when it starts to speak or is on the verge of starting to speak: the way the child's brain functions in order to produce speech makes it capable of new reasoning powers. As soon as the child speaks, "words and their relationships become the vehicles of his ideas and the keepers of his memories; now he is able to imagine what cannot be seen directly, and his mental capacities find themselves astonishingly augmented" (Viaud).

Confronted by a practical problem, the mute child tackles it in the same way as the monkey—by trial and error

[5] Recently Oleron, in the course of comparing deaf children with normal ones, came to the conclusion that in a number of tests it is not speech itself that is important for inducing the child's superiority over the monkey, but the cerebral development that permits it. Speech provides intellectual proficiency, and above all, it makes social acquisitions possible.

—and if he solves it, it is by chance, whereas the child who can speak grasps the problem's construction and solves it right away. Sometimes this can work out to the child's disadvantage, since if the problem is too difficult for his powers of reasoning the monkey may still be able to solve it by those random fumblings that the child has abandoned, and so he meets with a check by being too intelligent. On the other hand, if the problem requires the understanding of a principle, or a particular arrangement of objects, only the child who can speak will be able to solve it.

# *Part Two*

# *The Cerebral Mechanisms of Speech*

# 4 / The Speech Centers

## The Motor Control of Speech

Articulated human speech—a phenomenon of air vibration—is a special case of voluntary motor control: we have learned to coordinate the contraction of numerous muscles in our upper respiratory tract in such a way that the vibration of the air expelled produces characteristic sounds, and the emission of these various sounds, originally fortuitous, has become voluntary by virtue of audiophonatory conditioning, and this is now an automatic function in that we no longer have to think of the necessary movements. Briefly, the various factors are the respiratory muscles that control the intensity of the air current supplied to the larynx, which produces, mainly by means of the vocal cords, the *glottal* sound that is the voice's basic element. This sound is modified in the pharyngobuccal cavities to produce the harmonics necessary for the various *vowels* and to bring about the combinations of specific sounds that provide the *consonants* essential for the recognition of the spoken message; they are produced by modifications in the shapes imposed upon the higher air cavities by the muscles of the pharynx, the soft palate, the tongue, the lips, the cheeks and the masticatory muscles of the lower jaw. These various muscles only come into play under impulses of nervous energy supplied by their motive nerves and originating in the cerebral centers. They contract in response to various organic functions, and they are phonatory organs only when they are all under the control of the special neurons of the cerebral cortex; these neurons coordinate to share the impulses among them, so that each is affected to the degree necessary for phonation, and one such cerebral coordinative center is the speech center, or, more exactly, the motive center of articulated speech. Thus speech depends upon the cerebral cortex, and the reason why monkeys cannot speak although they have all the muscles necessary for speech is primarily because they have not enough coordinative neurons in their cerebral cortices to insure motor control of voice production.

There is nothing exceptional about speech as an organic function; it originates in the frontal convolution of the voluntary motor neurons controlling the body's various muscles, these neurons being more numerous when the muscle is capable of greater precision; the neurons controlling the phonatory muscles are found toward the lower part of the convolution, those responsible for the larynx, pharynx and tongue being particularly important as regards their number and the place they occupy in the convolution. The muscles on each side of the body have

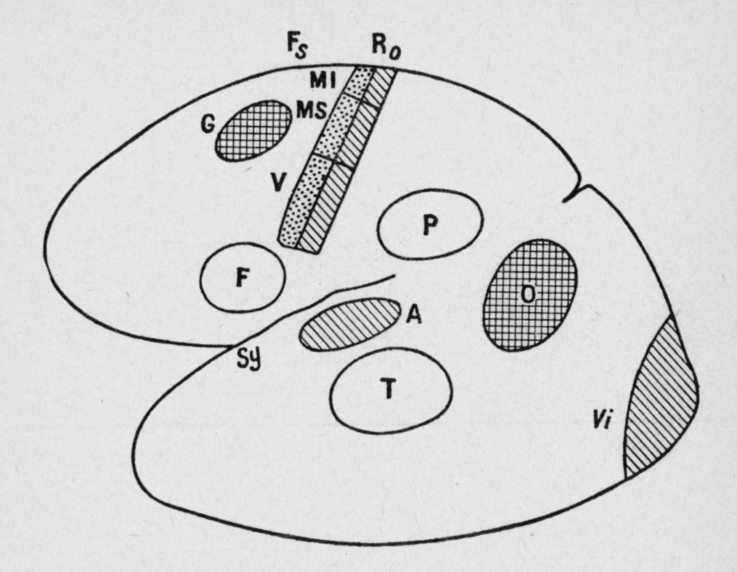


*The Cerebral Centers of Speech and Related Activities*

The diagram illustrates the outer surface of the left hemisphere, with the fissures of Rolando and Sylvius marked *Ro* and *Sy*. The dotted areas represent the motor centers, that marked *Mi* controlling the right leg and trunk, *Ms* the right arm and *V* the muscles of the face, tongue and larynx. i.e. those that effect mimicry and phonation, while the muscular and cutaneous sensitivity of those zones is controlled by the shaded area to the rear of Rolando's fissure. *F* represents Broca's area, that is, the center of articulation and articular control, *G* the center of manual control, including writing, and *Fs* the position of a supplementary center of articulation on the hemisphere's inner surface; the area marked *P* contains the gnosic center relating to the muscular sensitivity of the phonatory muscles, *A*, in the temporal zone, is the auditory center, *T*, the gnosic center of sounds as used in speech, *Vi*, in the occipital lobe, is the visual center, and *O* represents the gnosic center of verbal visualization, i.e. reading. The three unshaded areas are the speech centers as defined by Penfield. The zone responsible for language is bounded by *O, P, F* and *T*.

their cortical neurons on the opposite side, due to the axons of the cortical motor neurons crossing at the base of the brain; this formation is called the *decussation of the pyramids.* These axons do not lead directly to the muscles, but bring into play the peripheral motor neurons responsible for this innervation; these have their ends in contact with the nerve cells of their respective muscles at various points in the mid-brain, the *pons Varolii,* the bulb and the cervical medulla. Indeed it is only at the level of the brain that those neurons affecting phonation are in contact with one another; the peripheral neurons are far apart and their fibers reach the muscles by means of various nerves: the trigeminal nerve is responsible for jaw movements, the facial for the muscles of the face and the lips, the glossopharyngeal and the pneumogastric for the pharynx, the hypoglossal for the tongue, and, finally, the nerve fibers of the spine meet the pneumogastric nerve to control the larynx.

Though there are some rigidly defined areas corresponding to these executive agents that are the cortical motor neurons, they still do not comprise a speech center. This description, which goes back to observations made by Broca on an aphasiac (1861), must be reserved for those neurons responsible for the coordination of all the above-mentioned neurons; they are situated in the frontal zone immediately in front of the principal motive area, and are responsible for the harmony of the various articulatory controls. This control of a number of muscles for the purpose of carrying out a complex movement is not peculiar to speech, but is found in connection with all gestures.

In all cases, the centers of responsibility are situated in the frontal zone just in front of the motive area, and their existence is demonstrated by the effects produced when they are either stimulated or destroyed. The center responsible for coordinating the muscles of the hand in writing—and, indeed, in all complex actions, such as waving, typing, etc.—is situated above the speech center, and gestures of this sort are termed *praxes.* The centers of speech and of writing are only particular cases of praxic centers, and their lesion produces a failure of function that in the case of speech is motor aphasia or *anarthria* (loss of articulation) and, in the case of writing, *agraphia.*[1] Electrical excitation of the speech center during nerve surgery (the subject being conscious all the time since the brain is insensitive to pain) does not cause an involuntary release of sounds or words, but it prevents the subject from speaking. On the other hand, excitation of the motor area can induce an involuntary cry (Penfield); this also happens in a supplementary zone situated in front of the motor area on the hemisphere's internal face, which constitutes a secondary center of vocalization.

While the motor neurons involved in speech are situated in both hemispheres, the opposite is true of the coordinative centers of articulation such as writing: in the right-handed subject these are situated only on the left side, which then innervates the body's right side; and for the left-handed subject it is the other way round. This has to

[1] A distinction must be made between agraphia arising from a failure of function and agraphia brought on by a loss of graphic memory, which would involve, for instance, an inability even to spell out words with lettered blocks.

do with the *dominance* of one hemisphere over the other, and of this we so far know rather little, but it is clear that precise gestures require a single control center that is located in the preponderant hemisphere. Only injuries to that hemisphere will have an effect on speech.

The coordinative centers are not the seat of mysterious verbal or graphic motor images, but they contain the neuronic circuits involved in the remembering of the articulation of phonemes or the graphic forms of letters, and these constitute the channels employed by the conditioned reflexes formed during childhood that subsequently become automatic—those reflexes that can be inhibited by electrical excitation, although it cannot operate them.

Thus articulated speech is a function localized in a particular zone of the cerebral cortex, but since a motor control is involved, it will be subject to anything that can modify muscular condition and, in particular, to all impulses of whatever origin that connect with the motor neurons of the phonatory muscles, since the latter, like all motor neurons, are at the receiving end of a whole number of influences. The pyramidal control, which is the agent of voluntary movement, is a newcomer in biological evolution, and it is peculiar to those mammals that have a complex cerebral cortex *(neocortex)*. Before its appearance other motor neurons assured the voluntary motivity of the lower animals, and these neurons, dispossessed of that function, continued to exist in the higher mammals, but now they specialize in another aspect of motivity—involuntary automatic motivity. If the cortex is removed from mammals such as the dog or the cat, these neurons are sufficient to insure behavior patterns that are normal in appearance, but that are purely automatic. But in monkeys and in man they can only operate in association with the neurons of the cortex, which keep them strictly under their domination. These centers of automatic motivity are situated principally in the *corpus striatum,* the gray matter at the base of the brain. This region, which includes related formations such as the sensitive thalamus and the hypothalamus, which regulates organic activity, is the seat of nervous functions responsible for innate instinctive behavior and reflex manifestations of affectivity. If a dog lacking a cortex is roused, it shows increased fury, and it is still capable of barking, which suggests strongly that in the animal deprived of articulated language vocal control becomes a function of those centers. In man, articulation demands the intervention of the cortex, but there is considerable interaction between the cortex and the *corpus striatum:* certain neurons of the cortex called *extra-pyramidal* act upon the *corpus striatum,* into which they lead. In many cases of speech impediment the lesions are not solely at the level of the speech center, but also involve the *corpus striatum* (P. Marie). Our knowledge of these intricate mechanisms still lacks precision, but it is certain that the neuronic circuits of the speech center do not act directly upon the pyramidal neurons alone, but also on the underlying neurons of the *corpus striatum.* While the direct route is preponderant in the case of voluntary speech, the indirect route is important in automatic speech, which is the type of speech used most frequently by the adult: the *corpus striatum* intervenes in speech as in other types of learned motivity (swimming, etc.). Thus innate instinctive behavior such as walking or the affective cry, and acquired behavior that has become automatic, both have their seat in the *corpus striatum,* but the neurons of the cortex continue to intervene in acquired behavior. These mechanisms start to develop as soon as the child learns to modulate his affective birth cries.

Apart from the automatic motor control, a self-regulatory factor must also intervene, in speech as in all motor activities, to control the tensile state of the muscles according to need: the phonative muscles, like all other, are prepared in advance for the contraction that is about to be asked of them. For this purpose they are subject to the regulatory nerve centers, which coordinate the information received from the muscles themselves as regards their tensile state, from the vestibular sensitivity of the inner ear (balance), from the eye, and from the various motor centers, in particular from the cerebral cortex, which adjusts the tone of the various muscles according to what is required.[2] These centers, situated in the base of the brain, from the mid-brain to the bulb, include besides the *formatio reticularis,* the center of convergence of various impulses, control formations such as the red nucleus affecting muscular tone. The cerebellum, deriving from the red nucleus and receiving special messages from the muscular sensory system, and from the cerebral cortex, acts as a supplementary regulating organ that permits the extremely fine con-

[2] As regards the phonatory muscles, the tonic regulation is brought into play principally by messages from the sensory systems of the palate and the vibratory thorax, and above all by auditory messages.

trol of muscular tone, indispensable for the coordination of voluntary movement. Disease of the cerebellum (adiadochokinesis), which prevents muscular articulation and makes it impossible for sufferers to control the hand and forearm, also has as a consequence serious effects on writing and on speech, which becomes slow, irregular, explosive, brusque. Anything that affects the regulation of muscular tone will show itself by reacting upon speech, and there are numerous examples of this to be found in Garde's book *Begaiement*. It must be added that these regulating mechanisms also have the excitability of the cerebral cortex under their control: they include a regulatory factor in respect of sleeping and waking that keeps the cortex in a state of vigilance; thus all the finely adjusted directional controls necessary for the coordination of articular control tend to be disturbed by hypnotic inhibition (sleeplessness) originating from the centers at the base. The physiology of speech, which is a particular instance of the physiology of motivity, proves that although the essential element is the cortex's speech center, its satisfactory operation involves the intervention of extremely numerous neurological factors and also organic ones, such as the influence of hormones on the centers at the base in modifying the voice.

## *Internal Language and the Gnosic Aspect of Speech*

Having gone into the question of how the speech center performs its task, we must now consider how it is brought into play, and this is essentially a reflex action. The examination of these reflex messages will enable us to see to what extent speech in man has encroached upon the whole operation of the cerebral cortex. When we carry out a movement we are informed of it, apart from the evidence of our eyes and sometimes of our sense of balance (movements of the head), by our *muscular sensitivity;* this is not only the source of the unconscious regulation of muscular tone, but also provides the sense of position, or the sense of the recognition of form by touch, and it does this by impulses that it sends to the sensitive areas of the upper parietal zone by means of the motor localizations. The coordination of these messages by the neurons adjoining the parietal zone is necessary for the exercise of this recognition, and this process is termed *gnosia* by analogy with the executive praxes, and it is from injuries to these zones that an *agnosia* arises: the patient is unable to recognize an object by touch, even though he can analyze its qualities. The agnosiac is no more insensitive than the apraxiac is paralyzed, but he has lost an educative acquisition. This coordination of messages deriving from muscular sensitivity and from cutaneous sensitivity is also the source of a synthesis of the greatest importance for awareness, and this is the image we have of our bodies, our permanent conception of ourselves. The phonatory muscles (as well as the muscles involved in writing and gestures) also send messages of which we are more or less conscious: we are better able to identify the movements of the mouth and the tongue than those of the pharynx, and they contribute to the image of the body. Irrespective of our degree of awareness of this phenomenon, when we speak the muscular senses send an exact picture of the state of the phonatory muscles to the parietal cortex, and thus the parietal synthesis has a proprioceptive verbal image, just as when we write it receives an image of the movements necessary for forming the letters. It is not necessary to speak for a verbal image to exist in the cerebral cortex, and what one wants to say provides a pattern characteristic of neuronic relationships: the memory permits the evoking of recollections of these verbal images by the operation of our imagination. Once language has been acquired some very close relationships are established between the zone of parietal reception and the zone of motor execution that sustains the same image. It is sufficient to think of a word for the lips to frame it, and even if we refrain from this manifestation, it has been established that the internal thought is accompanied by an electrical activity of the phonatory muscles; and, among deaf-mutes accustomed to a gesture language, an analogous process has been observed in respect of the corresponding muscles.

Another sense has a part to play in speech, and this is the auditory sense: our ears analyze the sounds we utter and the auditory tract carries a signal response to the cerebral cortex, conveying the intensity, the level and the other characteristics of the sound it has received. It is the temporal zone that receives these messages and extracts from them a conscious synthesis, and the neurons in the vicinity of this receiving zone specialize in perceptive interpretation of the sound messages: in man, this is the zone of *auditory gnosia,* which, when subjected to excitation, produces some auditory hallucinations that can go so far as to revive memories (Penfield). That is to say, the subject believes that he hears a particular tune, or such-and-such a word. Damage to this zone does not produce deafness, but a failure to recognize the sense of sounds, i.e. an *auditory agnosia.* There are several types of auditory agnosia, which can show themselves separately or in combination: an agnosia of noises that are heard but not identified, an agnosia in respect of music (tone deafness), and, lastly, an agnosia as regards language itself, which seems to be an unknown foreign tongue *(verbal deafness,* a particular form of agnosia). Auditory gnosia has a special importance for the satisfactory functioning of speech, and there is a close relationship between the three speech centers, the frontal, the parietal and the temporal: for us, the spoken word is not only the memory of a motor activity, but is also an auditory memory. In the brain the word acquires its own personality, irrespective of the aspect of it that is most apparent to our consciousness: it is represented by a particular picture resulting from neuronic interconnections that involve, temporally and spatially, the whole central region of the hemisphere between the parietal, temporal and frontal zones, thus forming an enlarged language zone that is not affected by stimuli or localized lesions by reason of the alternative routes that the impulses can take; this is the internal speech zone, where the words originate that we use in our thinking.[3] In man, the

[3] This zone plays its part whether the thought is spoken or not spoken, since it is the zone that controls the articulative frontal center that gives birth to speech. In aphasia its operation is disturbed more as regards the voluntary aspect of speech than as regards its automatic manifestations.

excitation of the two parietal and temporal zones of verbal gnosia provokes, as in the excitation of the frontal zone, a transitory aphasia. Strictly speaking, these are the three speech centers. It must be clearly realized that these centers of verbal gnosia are themselves restricted to the one dominant hemisphere.

The brain of civilized man is rendered still more mobile by verbal symbolism, and indeed it is by means of what is involved in this that he learns to write. We have seen that this implicates a fresh activity for the frontal and parietal zones, but above all what is brought into play is a new cortical area: the understanding of the graphic gestures, together with what devolves from them, leads to reading, and therefore to an education in the recognition of visual forms. The occipital area that receives these visual messages is attended by an area of coordination that is the seat of the gnosic interpretations: excitation of this area produces visual hallucinations and a lesion of it induces agnosias. Among the latter is found an agnosia in respect of the written word, that is, *verbal blindness* (the patient no longer knows how to read), and this devolves from a zone close to the parietal and temporal speech centers. Moreover, reading also makes use of the parietal proprioceptive messages, which, preceding from the eye muscles, contribute to an understanding of the forms and their visual significance.

A consideration of the speech centers enables the cerebral localizations to be put in their correct place: it is not the function that is localized, nor is the process of thought placed above that of speech; what are localized are the mechanisms of execution and reception, damage to which causes irreducible disturbances; in this sense, speech centers do indeed exist, but speech is insured by the innumerable relationships set up among the centers that together involve the operation of the greater part of the cortex. It is from various aspects—motor, proprioceptive, auditory and even visual, all imposing the same symbols at several entrances and exits of the cerebral cortex—that speech is enabled to act as a vehicle for thought.[4] Thus the code of signal responses is spread over the whole internal functioning of the cortex by natural means.

[4] The external world's other signals do not lend themselves nearly so well to such a role. Nevertheless an inclination towards abstraction and generalization also concerning the various gnosias is much more developed in man than in animals.

# 5 / *The Secondary System of Signals*

Human intelligence has devised the power of representing by an articulated sound signal all the various things in the world, and this code of sounds has shown itself to be extremely convenient for the furtherance of the thought processes since, although originally a product of voluntary motor activity, it has become an aspect of the cerebral function. This revolutionary innovation, a consequence of the brain's supreme importance to the world and to itself, even before it could play a causal part, does not involve any modification of structure or of function of the cerebral cortex. Fundamentally, speech has no physiology of its own: the speech centers are specializations of praxic and gnosic centers already existing in animals, and those familiar with motor and sensory physiology and pathology can conjecture their application to speech. Similarly, on the plane of cerebral physiology, speech relies on the normal machinery for insuring the higher nervous activity: it depends upon a process of apprenticeship and of memory, and in consequence it obeys the laws of the conditioned reflexes. When Pavlov began his researches, he concerned himself neither with man nor with speech, and yet the scientific study made by him upon the established phenomena of training, in which he determined quantitatively the variations of the brain's excitability by evaluating the amount of saliva secreted during a conditioned reflex, led him to an appreciation of the functioning of the cerebral cortex that explained, as he came to recognize in due course, the whole physiology of language. Before that, hypothetical stores of verbal images had been envisaged and were supposed, according to an unacceptable localizing materialism, to be seated in the neurons of the various cerebral zones. Experiments on conditioned reflexes, without elucidating the basis of the memory, have shown us it in its true light; it is not immaterial but purely functional, providing the means for a neuronic architecture, that is, for an assembly of nervous connections that, once established in the cerebral cortex, reestablishes itself whenever the conditions renew themselves, though showing no trace of its existence in the interval.[1] A word is not some mysterious substance stored in a neuron. It is a particular aspect of functional relationships existing between millions of neurons. There is no fundamental difference in functional machinery between our thought processes and the mechanical thought of the great electronic computers: in

[1] We are still very ignorant of the exact nature of this process and of its renewals of activity.

both instances electric waves transmit a coded message and the circulation of the impulses in a closed circuit act on the basis of the immediate memory. Grey Walter has been able to provide his electronic tortoise with supplementary machinery, allowing it to acquire an elementary conditioned reflex. What comprises the originality of the human brain is its power of integration originating from its grasp of consciousness, and there is also the fact that its mechanisms were not given to it, but constructed themselves in the course of development; in this man is in marked contrast to the machine,while only differing from animals by virtue of his much greater complexity.

When our mouths water upon hearing the word "apple" instead of at the sight of an apple, nothing is changed on the physiological plane: the harmonized play of the inverse processes of stimulation and inhibition in the cerebral cortex and its spatio-temporal modifications lead to the recognition of the signal that induces the reaction which, before conditioning, had no connection with it. "The processes of stimulation and of inhibition, of irradiation, of concentration and of reciprocal induction, the whole of this complex dynamic of the physiological processes that are produced in the cortex" unfolds itself, as Pavlov has shown, in the same way for the verbal conditioned reflexes as for the other types. Moreover, as regards speech, there exists a whole hierarchy of increasingly complex conditionings. For a start, there are the conditioned reflexes arising from muscular and auditory sensitivity, which permit the child to learn to utter the desired phonemes and to reproduce those that he hears.

These are followed by verbal symbolism as a whole, and then come the grammatical relationships and usages that enable us to construct comprehensible phrases. At all these levels it would be interesting to know about the cerebral processes that take place: the science of psychophysiological linguistics ought not to restrict itself to the study of the phonemes of various languages or to the study of vocabulary, but as Husson has suggested, it should investigate the high-level structures that represent what is essential in every language. With the support of Sauvageot's works, Husson urges the physiological importance of the *syntagmatic* relationships, such as the relationship between the subject and the verb.

Although on the physiological plane language does not differ from the other conditioned reflexes, it was to Pavlov's credit that he demonstrated that it nevertheless presents a very particular aspect of conditioning, specific to man, that establishes objectively the superiority of his psychology. Language is considered by Pavlov and his followers as "the secondary system of signals" and, by taking into consideration its characteristics and the relationships it maintains with the primary system—that is, the system of non-verbal signals, which is the only one that exists among animals—allows some very interesting insights into human psychology. In 1924 Pavlov wrote: "As regards man, speech is clearly a conditioned stimulus as real as all those that he has in common with animals, but on the other hand, it goes further than they go and, like no other stimulus, it embraces a multitude of purposes. In this connection, speech allows no comparison, either qualitative or quantitative, with the conditioned stimuli of animals." In 1932 he returned to the subject: "If our sensations and our observations as regards the world about us constitute for us the first signals of reality, the concrete signals, it is speech and, above all, the kinesthetic stimuli (muscular sensitivity) linking the speech organs with the cortex that constitute the secondary signals, the signals that devolve from signals. They represent an abstraction of reality and lend themselves to a superior generalization, which is exactly what constitutes our specifically human method of supplementary thought."

A dog can be trained to react to the word "bell," but the actual ringing of a bell would not produce the same reaction: for the dog, the word has no value except as a signal it has been trained to respond to, and it has no general abstract significance that will enable the animal to replace it by the sound of a bell. On the other hand, a man trained to react to a bell can react in the same way to the word "bell," or to a synonym of it: "The relationship between the word and the thing is certainly acquired during ontogenesis, but contrary to what happens as regards the secondary reflexes of a dog (where the animal, trained to react to one signal, learns to react to a second signal associated with the first) it is both independent of any particular experience, and common to all those who speak the same language. The concrete object that signals the total stimulus is signaled by the word. The word is a signal of a signal. The word belongs to a whole (the language), which constitutes the secondary system of signals; this is the system that signals the primary system constituted by the concrete reality of the object. The secondary system of signals unites the different forms of the specific signaling of the higher nervous activity of man, in accordance with the general laws of analysis and synthesis of the cerebral cortex, but this on the basis of the particular material that is the objective reality existing independently of the individual, who speaks, writes, listens or reads, and is subject to language that has its own laws" (Follin). Pavlov's pupil, Ivanov Smolenski, who studied these questions in detail, said: "What is produced in the secondary system of signals is the *verbal reflection* of the external and internal environment, and it is also the reflection of the primary system of signals that perceives these environments at first hand.... The whole ontogenic history, socially determined, of the development of man's higher nervous activity—from the simplest forms to the most complex of its higher forms—is reflected in the common activity and reciprocal action of the two systems of signals."

The unity between the dynamic structure of a word and the thing designated is insured by a process termed *elective irradiation,* and numerous experiments at various ages have enabled the relationships between the two systems to be established. When the ringing of a bell produces a reaction in a sympathetic province that is normally beyond the control of the will—pupillary dilation, for instance—the word "ringing" is also effective, which shows the power of the word in psychosomatic phenomena. If a positive conditioned reaction is created to the words "wild beast" and a negative one to "bird" all words designating wild beasts, wolf, tiger, etc., become positive, and all bird names negative, which indicates the importance of words as regards generalization. The psychiatric technique in which the subject must give a word-for-word account of his behavior indicates how far toward the secondary system, that of awareness, the subject has gone. In the development of the child after the stage in which only the primary system exists, as with animals, the stage of comprehension marks a linking of the secondary system to the primary, and the stage at which speech begins shows a connection in the opposite direction, since it is only slowly that the child gives a verbal response to verbal stimulations. "In the course of the child's development everything that takes place in the primary system of signals acquires a reflex in the secondary system that is always more complete and precise, and direct experience becomes more and more susceptible to abstraction and generalization. . . . Nevertheless even in adults a certain part of experience, varying with different individuals, can remain for a time without moving into the secondary system. In such cases, verbal definition and enunciation are not possible, and consciousness remains incomplete" (Ivanov Smolenski).

In man, the role of the secondary system predominates over that of the primary, but since its acquisition is more recent it is also more fragile, and it is the first to disappear in hypnotic states, such as are induced by fatigue or intoxication: the inhibitions incurred during sleep overpower the secondary system and transitorily strengthen the primary, as is shown by dreams, and it is the same during hysteria. Thus numerous experiments on some of Pavlov's pupils defined precisely to what extent the process of verbalization is influenced by fatigue, by various mental disturbances, and by drugs that either stimulate or sedate the nervous system. The elective sensitivity of the secondary system does not imply that it depends upon different centers, but that it stands in a more delicate relationship with the physiological processes, and one that demands a better condition of the cerebral cortex. To quote Pavlov, "The over-all condition of mental health and of the ego's integrity lies in the normal functioning of the two systems, their cohesion and interdependence." The various types of equilibrium in this respect enable the nervous types of both man and child to be defined.

Equally, it has been shown that there are some processes peculiar to man even in the primary system of signal responses.[2] "It can be supposed," writes Elkonin, "that man's most characteristic trait is precisely his ability to create new relationships between things." A child, almost from the outset, can make new constructions by a process of generalization; the child deduces what he should do from what he has been taught, and he quickly adapts himself to new conditions, either by means of signal responses or by means of his executive mechanisms: 28 per cent of correct solutions were provided by children aged between five and six, but 80 per cent by children of ten to twelve. It would be interesting to know what would be the proportion of correct solutions before the acquisition of

[2] There is an equivalence between the primary system and Pichon's *sensuactorielle* thought.

speech. It should be added that imitation also constitutes an excellent means of education for the child.

Thus it is seen now that the human brain has succeeded in constructing a totally new psychology upon a physiology identical to that of an animal's brain. Karl Marx wrote: "What distinguishes the worst architect from the cleverest bee is the fact that the first has built a cell in his head before realizing it in wax." Something that would not be possible without words.

"Not only does the secondary system of signals allow the transmission of acquired knowledge throughout the whole length of the historical process by which man has gradually made himself nature's master, but it also provides him with a means of knowledge, and enables him to abstract profound significance from the primary signals received by him from reality, and to examine the laws that govern nature's purposes. The secondary system is not knowledge... but a means of knowledge, a powerful means, and it is also a means of creation."

# 6 / *Speech and Consciousness*

When, at about two-and-a-half, the child starts to refer to himself as "I" he has become fully conscious, he has finally surpassed the psychological level of the animal, and this is the result of his persevering efforts to gain mastery over speech, which is a cultural process. Thus the degree of reflective consciousness attained by man is linked to speech; it is because thought is internal language that it is communicable, and that psychology, the science of the states of consciousness, has been made possible. Without taking up a position on the metaphysical viewpoint in which science can never predominate, it can be said that the unacceptable dualism of Plato and Descartes, which rigidly separated man's soul from his body (in contrast to the sane and realistic monism of Aristotle and St. Thomas Aquinas), was in error when it dissociated the psychological from the physiological and made the brain an instrument of the soul. It is nothing of the sort, and in those conditions of incarnation in which the soul shows itself to be an information of structure, it is the cerebral aspect that gives birth to the psychological aspect. For a long time it was asked how two such incompatible orders of fact could be linked, and all the ancient materialists could do was to deny transcendance and the peculiarities of the human psyche. That this is no longer so is due principally to the physiological attitude to speech, whereby it is considered as the secondary system of signals. "It can now be said that unity has been achieved between the objective world and man's subjective world. The predominant role of the secondary system of signals, and its unity with the primary system, form the basis of man's unity, which has at last ceased to be torn between consciousness and body" (Follin). It is no longer a question of submitting psychology to physiology, but of explaining how physiology gives birth to psychology, which nevertheless retains all its originality. "The brain's reflex activity," Rubinstein tells us, "is at one and the same time a nervous (physiological) activity and a psychological one, since it is the *same* activity examined from the point of view of different relationships. This is why it must be studied first as regards nervous activity (a process of stimulation and inhibition, irradiation, concentration and reciprocal induction) and, secondly, as regards psychological activity (a process of perception and observation, memory, thought, etc.). Each science studies the manifestations of reality from the viewpoints relevant to it. As regards physiology, reality appears as a collection of stimuli acting upon the analyzing factors and the brain, whereas from the psychological viewpoint it is the *objects* of thought and action that appear as reality, the objects to which man is related as *subject*.... The mutual relationships between the science of psychology and the study of the higher nervous activities fit into the over-all framework of relationships situated between the 'higher' branches of scientific knowledge and the 'lower.' "

Relationships between the internal language—that psychological process whose physiological basis we now understand—and consciousness exist on the two different planes that characterize the higher nervous activity; on the one hand there is the analytical plane of the thought's instantaneous flow, and on the other hand there is the plane that is often neglected, but that nevertheless constitutes consciousness' most important aspect: this plane is concern with the integrative synthetic activity of the nervous system, which prevents the higher nervous activity from being merely the sum total of a number of conditioned reflexes, and forms from it a personal reflective consciousness capable of control and mastery. The word, which is the tool of consciousness, is also a means of consciousness.

## *The Verbalization of Thought*

That physiology confirms those conclusions of psychoanalysis shows that our consciousness has a restricted field; we are conscious only of what we give our attention to; what is beyond our immediate attention, as well as that immense area which is impenetrable, constitutes the subconscious, and this forms the greater part of our psychological structure and cerebral activity. The physiology of consciousness in man is not fundamentally different from that of animals: it invariably involves two degrees, one being the state of vigilance of the cerebral cortex conditioned principally by the regulatory center at the base of the brain, and the other being the attentive process, which involves a higher degree of consciousness applying to only a small part of the brain's total awareness. Although full consciousness, and even the waking state itself in man and monkey, is not possible except with the cooperation of the cerebral cortex, it does not follow that everything which takes place at the cortex's level is conscious. Formerly it was thought that if the organic visceral area escaped consciousness and the will almost entirely, it was because the higher neurons regulating organic activity were situated at the level of the hypothalamus, their connections with the cerebral cortex being only indirect. Today, however, thanks to both the study of the cortico-visceral conditioned reflexes and to the study of the effects of stimulation of the cortex—and the registering of the potentials evoked—it is known that there is a visceral brain, and that either in certain special areas, or at the level of the motor and sensory representations involved in the relationship structure there are neurons that receive and send organic messages, which in general bypass consciousness: the nervous system constitutes a whole even in its highest levels. Bykov's researches have shown clearly that the laws of cerebral functioning do not depend upon whether a reaction is conscious or unconscious: in the cerebral cortex there are conditioned reflexes both in the unconscious organic area and in the conscious area, as well as some compound reflexes that link the relational aspect and the nutritional aspect. The researches entirely ignored the point of view of the consciousness, which should nevertheless be taken into consideration, since it provides an important avenue of approach as regards the physiology of consciousness. It seems that a reaction's conscious character depends upon its ability not to stay localized, but to take part in the integrated function of the cortex. All local processes are excluded from the cortical integration, and thus from consciousness: their intensity is too slight to be important, and this implies that the neurons brought into play are either too few or have a frequency too different from that of the other neurons; this is the case as regards the sympathetic cortical neurons. It is not difficult for this unconscious part of the cortex to establish contact with the organic centers at the base of the brain, and this explains why the viscera respond to unconscious psychological reactions: a certain amount of conflict exists between the activated part of the cerebral function—the seat of conscious psychology grounded upon the outside world as regards the relational aspect—and the inhibited or nonactivated part, which, excluded from consciousness, is in contact with the organic sphere, the instincts and the affections. This distinction between the two spheres is also found in animals, but in a lesser degree than in man; psychosomatic disorders are less important in the animal, since its degree of consciousness is relatively weak. If it is otherwise in man, with his greater cerebral development, it is because the conscious sphere is essentially the sphere of verbalized thought. For man to become conscious of something is, above all, to name it; everything pertaining to the primary system analogous to animal thought only becomes fully conscious if it can be transposed into the secondary system and expressed in the code of external speech that we have learned to use for expressing thought. Now speech, as a means of communication between men, is mainly practical when it aims at communal action; in daily life there is no need at all for us to verbalize the organic sphere, whose functions proceed automatically without our thinking about them. It is in the sphere of the concrete—and in generalization and abstractions arising from it—that human consciousness has developed to facilitate the relationship between the two systems of signals, and this is so even as regards the most abstruse scientific speculations using mathematical language. Conversely, when what is at issue does not fall within the province of our senses, the deficiencies of verbal expression go hand in hand with lesser consciousness: this happens not only in the organic sphere, but also in the spheres of the instincts and affections, where the shortcomings of speech have long been acknowledged. Feeling that these realities are beyond a rational description, we seek to express our intuitions and sentiments by another system of signals, whose values are essentially artists—poets and painters—strive toward a surreality, and endeavor to communicate what is incommunicable. Similarly, the believer in mystical experience forsakes dogmatic formulations as being incapable of expressing the whole of humanly inaccessible reality as he perceives it in the course of his transcendental aspirations, only to find himself in a "dark night" where God's presence resides more in what he is not than in what he is. A fair proportion of the debates between believers and non-believers may be put down to the inadequacies of language, since no proofs, no demonstrations and no arguments of real analogical value are enough to transmit faith, which is the incommunicable certainty of divine existence. They attempt to put into words what cannot humanly be put into words, which has nonetheless been called the Word; they lead the non-believer to a legitimate criticism of a too-humanized God, who may often be the false magical image wrongly offered by believers to represent their faith, but who is not the true God. Healthy tolerance, based on an agnosticism that allows that, apart from personal experience belief and non-belief are equally tenable on the material plane, is trammeled by the inadequacies of language.

The vast province of the subconscious explored by psychoanalysis, in which everything that during childhood has affected the emotional structure, or has prevented spontaneous tendencies from expressing themselves, or has established on grounds provided by heredity the true foundations of our character, which will condition the apparently unforseeable behavior of the adult, is essentially the province of the unformulated, of the non-verbal, precisely because it goes back to a period at which the mechanism of speech was yet to be perfected, and because it adjoins an area in which speech is impotent. Neurogenic suppressions and sublimations, and preventative or curative introductions to consciousness, find their justification in cerebral physiology and particularly in the study of conditioned reflexes. Here, too, intercourse between the consciousness and the subconscious necessarily involves verbalization: the point is to formulate in language memories charged with emotion that the protective conditioned inhibitions have eliminated from consciousness, but that betray their presence by disturbing the whole psychological structure or by causing organic disorders, and, again, speech is necessary for recovering the hidden meanings embedded in verbal lapses and formulations that are an aspect of the relationship existing between the two systems of signals. Under the conscious meaning of what we say there is often a hidden meaning: without exaggerating or attributing an importance to something that is at times only coincidence, without falling into those excesses of theory that mythically equate sex with the whole subconscious, it is nonetheless certain that we often obey subconscious motivations, and that the reasons that we give for our behavior are not always the right ones.

It is when consciousness relaxes, in dreams, or better still, during the hypnotic states when the cerebral function becomes incoherent, that it loses its mastery of speech, and then the primary system becomes preponderant and the subconscious has the best chance of expressing itself. At such times the whole psychological content reveals itself, which explains the interest in dream analysis and the use of analysis under drugs. Nevertheless it remains rather difficult to understand the message of the subconscious precisely, since the doctor's consciousness, or that of the patient recalling his dream, attempts to rationalize or to formulate in words what cannot be formulated. The dream is a form of primitive thought expressed basically in images where speech plays only a feeble role, although it interposes itself later when the subject recollects his dream upon waking.

If the subconscious reacts upon consciousness by trying to put itself into words, thus suppressing the anguish of what is unexpressed, the converse is also true: by virtue of the cerebral unity between consciousness and the subconscious, language affects the sphere of the subconscious. *Suggestion*—all-powerful as regards certain passive subjects—persuasion and the grasp of consciousness are extremely active even in the organic sphere. The power of suggestion in hysteria, whether for provoking or for allaying disturbances, is well known, but it is during sleep and related states that suggestion is at its most effective, since then the link between consciousness and the subconscious is closer. The influence of speech upon the organic functions in man has been demonstrated in Bykov's experiments: verbal suggestion can progressively reverse an organic reflex. It is recognized that suggestion can get rid of organic formations such as warts, and that blisters can be produced by suggesting a burn. All this confirms that the influence of the spoken word goes beyond the area of conscious cerebral activity, and reacts also upon the subconscious part of cerebral activity based upon the sphere of the organic. Modern psychosomatic medicine, born of psychoanalysis although receiving its expository physiological basis from the Pavlovian researches, shows clearly that in man especially the medical treatment of organs is not possible unless the diseased organ is thought of as being subject to the influence of the brain, the psychological state and the spoken word, and this is true both for the sickness and for its cure. The pangs of childbirth do not depend solely upon the violence of the muscular contractions, but to a large extent upon the conditioned reflexes that have been set up by fear: when the woman who has learned midwifery and is aware of the processes of childbirth participates actively in the birth, the pangs tend to disappear by virtue of their relationship with the cerebral physiology, and the reasons for this appear both in the Pavlovian studies and in the electrophysiological experiments conducted by Fulton and his pupils.

Thus total consciousness in man is linked to language, what is not put into words is not brought out into the clear light of reflection, and when it is forced to find expression in the neuronic circuits of the brain, either it is driven back into an organic manifestation of a pathological nature, or it isolates itself in the cerebral disturbances of the neurosis. Yet not the whole province of language is conscious: speech is an automatic function that does not require attentive consciousness[1] and we think without noticing that we are thinking, just as we no longer need to attend to the complex mechanisms of articulation. At the same time it is possible for us to give attention to the

[1] Our subsequent observations on the aphasias will show the importance of this distinction between automatic and voluntary speech.

unfolding of our thoughts, and then we see some mental images that have relevant auditory or motor qualities, to a greater or lesser degree; this is an aspect of the complex cerebral function that is the basis of internal speech. There is no such thing as pure thought without cerebral functioning, without internal speech, and without images. Outside of sleep and related states, and even within them (dreams), we are constantly thinking, but the greater part of our thoughts remain subconscious. The subconscious is not only what is not expressed in words; it is also that which is so expressed, but to which we have paid no attention; as regards our intuitions, sudden ideas and subconscious messages, it is difficult to say exactly which of them devolve from verbalized subconscious thought, and which from thoughts that have been formed from unverbalized images. For instance, we know that a lesson read last thing at night can become fixed in the memory during sleep, and there is no doubt that here the verbal mechanisms have continued to function subconsciously. As long as man thinks, as long as his brain functions, he will remain man—a being capable of internal language even if his consciousness is clouded, and even if the second system of signal responses loses its preponderance.

### *The Verbalization of the Ego*

What characterizes human consciousness is that it is reflective, that it is truly "consciousness of consciousness." We are not merely the passive vessels of our thought and action, we are not, like animals, unable to detach ourselves sharply from the present moment: being conscious, we can detach ourselves, we can stand back from the present, and we can separate the thought from its thinker to establish an ego that can direct and assess its thought process at one and the same time to the past, the present and the future. Such is the higher form of consciousness specific to man, and apparently having little in common with animal thought. The animal stands apart from us not only because it does not use words and has no internal speech that can be expressed by external speech, but also because it has no control over its thought processes and does not reflect in the human manner.[2] It would be a mistake to see in the human's reflective consciousness a mysterious power superimposed upon the brain; without inferring any metaphysical consequences, it is verbalization that must be seen as the factor which allows the exploitation of mankind's reflective consciousness by virtue of man's larger brain.

To become conscious of anything is to integrate a cerebral process into the brain's collective functioning. The idea of our ego is with us permanently, and we especially connect it with our body's image on the basis of our current feelings and our memory of the past; this image of the ego, resulting from the cerebral process, combines with a rather intense localized cerebral process to provide the basis of awareness when we pay attention to something. Animals possess such a mechanism, and they can pay attention, but

[2] Animal powers of reflection such as are revealed by the rat (Maier) in associating elements that have been taught it, or by the monkey in making tools, remain extremely rudimentary.

the difference between man and animal is that man's image of his body, because verbalized, becomes the ego, just as the spoken word has acquired an existence independent of the object it represents and is capable of an individual life (this being, as we have seen, the basis of thought). It is particularly significant that the child's reflective consciousness only reveals itself when the child becomes capable of referring to himself as "I," that is, when the child sees himself as a thinking entity who is master of his thought processes. This detachment of the verbalized ego from the real is so strong that it happens even in dreams: the ego of a dream, unrelated to external reality in the detachment of sleep, watches with astonishment the unreal spectacle of the images unfolding incoherently. The stages of the ego's construction in the child can be followed: the process starts with the child's discovery of his body when he is still at the animal stage; and the ego that establishes itself as being separate from all others is provided by those others with the possibility of a real and separate existence through language.[3] The relationship of the subjective and objective self toward others (first of all the parents) is far more responsible for originating neurotic disturbances than are repressions of a sexual nature such as are overemphasized by Freudian psychoanalysis. The

[3] Even in the absence of language, the superiority of the integrative power of the human brain over that of animals allows man to have an actually lower degree of consciousness, which is something not easy to appreciate. It is the development of the prefrontal zone, the critical organ responsible for the most human qualities, such as free will and love, that gives primitive man, even lacking an elaborate language, an immense superiority over animals.

verbalization of memories, which gives recollection its human dimension, plays a great role in the growing awareness of the ego: only man enjoys the possession of his past in the form of a true-life story, with its succession of days and years marked out by chronological milestones. By means of the verbalized ego a true personality is acquired, and this acquisition, by its eclectic attributes and its control of a thought process that is also verbalized, is the source of moral consciousness: man formulates plans in his thoughts before carrying them out; he envisages what he should do by referring to an ideal whose elements are provided by society, but upon which he exercises his selective powers, feeling that even if he does not know what to do, he ought to do something since he is a human being. That is to say, he feels both free and responsible. The source of freedom is the potentiality of the reflective consciousness to master motives; an animal caught between inclinations of equal force is unaware of its freedom to choose since it is incapable of real judgment. Man alone, although completely ruled by motive, is free to the degree that he is conscious; his freedom, the product of man's greater brain, founders in the physiological, psychological and social motives that automate or disturb the function of the brain. The motives that threaten to submerge our arbitrary freedom must in no way be denied, and we must learn to recognize which supposed sins originate from pathological disorder and can be treated with therapy; but we must not suppose from this that freedom is illusory: on the contrary, a thorough understanding of motives and the reduction of their power leads to a freedom that is not license or apathy, but that incurs an obligation to yield to a higher motive to behave as a man, to embrace what is good and avoid what is evil; these are biological considerations that are highly effective in confirming the obscure intuitions of the moral sense.

All human psychopathological changes turn upon the derangement of the ego, and constitute a pathology of a consciousness that has lost the mastery of itself to a greater or lesser degree under the influence of disturbances that do not originate from some mysterious spirit, but comprise generalized changes in the cerebral function. We are less well informed about these than we are about the localized neurological lesions, yet our therapeutic treatment of them, although often inadequate and nearly always empirical, has nevertheless produced results: access to the causes of the disturbances has been gained either by neurological means (the technique of shock therapy in sleep), or by psychological means, that is to say, by the spoken word.

Parallel with the ego, which devolves from the integration of the conscious and verbalized conditionings, there is the possibility of an integration of the subconscious conditionings, giving a subconscious motivation to sublimated conduct of a kind acceptable to the conscience, and this is the physiological mechanism that is the basis of the Freudian *superego,* which is a superego insofar as it imposes its subconscious directives, but whose structure is, in fact, on a much lower level than that of the conscious ego. It attains true verbalized consciousness in disorders of the schizophrenic type. Language is so important for man that he does not make his more important decisions by means of subconscious and unformulated thought, but instead discusses them with himself in a form of dialogue, during which, in the depths of his being, he meets his ideal self in the form of a secret interlocutor; this is the voice of conscience, susceptible to pathological derangement. As Pavlov wrote, language "represents the regulatory system of human conduct."

# *Part Three*

# *Man without Speech*

# 7 | *The Isolated Ones*

The adult man, proud of his power of thought and of his conscience, wraps himself in his individualism and completely forgets that it is to society that he owes those very qualities of thought and consciousness. Yet it needs no imagination at all to envisage how poor and bestial human thought would be if it were deprived of language: and, indeed, there are men who cannot speak, and others who are deficient in speech. Disturbances of the power of speech are legion, and their degrees are extremely various, but since here we are studying language in its relation to thought we shall not deal with those deficiencies that derive purely from faults in articulation without any deficiency in the intelligence. It is the internal language that is the object of our study, rather than speech as a means of communication, but, as we shall see, disturbances of the internal language are always accompanied by related troubles in the external language, either by causing difficulty in evoking the right words although articulation is unimpaired, or by causing defects in the articulation itself. For a start, in trying to represent man deprived of language, we must not encroach upon the sphere of the truly pathological, but, instead, concentrate upon that of the normal, of the brain that has every potentiality and aptitude for speech. For a man to be unable to speak it is enough for him to have been withdrawn from the normal human environment as a child and thus never to have heard anyone speak. Two possibilities are involved—one is the case of the *isolated* child who has never come in contact with the human voice, and the other is that of the *deaf* child cut off by reason of his infirmity. In both cases the aptitude for speech as regards the brain's potentialities has not disappeared. The child, isolated or deaf, will presently reach the age when he would normally learn to modulate his cries and invent human phonemes, but when the deaf child is compared to the isolated one, he is at a disadvantage, since he is not able to hear his own voice, and for him to prattle simply for the sake of feeling the play of his throat muscles is not enough to hold his attention to any degree: such sounds remain weaker than in the hearing child, and although deaf children remain able to amuse themselves for quite a long time by uttering sounds whose existence they can deduce from the vibratory sensations of their phonatory organs, together with muscular sensations and perhaps the sight of their lips in mirrors—comparing these factors with the same factors in those who want to communicate with them—on the whole they give up the habit quite soon, and the motivation is too weak for their attempts at speech to develop. The isolated child can amuse himself by uttering sounds and hearing them, but he is as deprived as the deaf child in regard to the principal factor that helps to develop language in the child brought up in normal social conditions, which is, of course, the speech of those about him. Primitive man, from the most distant of prehistoric times, although still unable to speak, found incentives in his society, familial or tribal, for the development of vocal signals, which he needed either to establish relations, or to further a communal task, and then in due course, by means of a process that must have been extremely long, he invented speech and, little by little, acquired an internal language. Although present-day savages have come a long way from their original state, their languages are still simpler than ours and less subtle, and their thought processes, except as regards their immediate needs, are rudimentary. Nevertheless, as we have said, their potentialities at birth are equal to ours. The isolated man, on the other hand, has no reason to create his own language, as is sometimes done by children and the insane, since he has no one to communicate with. Utterly deprived of society, he rapidly becomes totally inept at language through having no way at all of making his brain work in human fashion. To quote Teilhard de Chardin, "From the moment in which the phyletic fibers start to conform to the pattern of the Noosphere's first lineaments, a new womb is formed around the child, and from then on this womb cannot be damaged without gravely mutilating the physical constitution of his biological being." The isolated child without human contact is no longer man, since man is a social being by definition and, in spite of the human nature of the child's biological constitution, he is dehumanized[1] and his brain, not fully developed, does not learn to function in a human environment and becomes incapable of doing so at the end of a few years. Thus, isolated man cannot be compared to the savage, who lives in a cultural environment that is nonetheless a human social environment in spite of its lower level, and even the savage does not retain all his potentialities throughout childhood, since after his sixth year he can no longer be fully absorbed into a higher culture.

## *Wolf-Reared Children and Segregated Children*

It is only recently that it has been possible to entertain any certainties regarding isolated man deprived of language. Legends relating to wild men have been current for centuries, and in 1758 Linnaeus qualified these creatures as *mutus, tetrapus* and *hirsutus,* and of these legends a particularly insistent one was that concerning children reared by wolves like Romulus and Remus. In 1940, Zingg cited thirty-one cases dating back to 1344 of children reared by animals, or at least growing up after being abandoned, but unfortunately no serious scientific observations had

[1] In his non-verbalized thought, which also develops socially, as in his verbalized thought.

been made. With regard to abandoned children, there is an interesting story in the case of Kaspar Hauser, the "wild boy" of Nuremberg: in 1828 he was found wandering about in Nuremberg at the age of sixteen, with a distracted and bewildered air. His origins have remained open to conjecture, but it was believed that he was abandoned and brought up by a laborer who had taught him reading, writing and the Christian religion but had kept him closely confined. The boy was educated and worked as a clerk until his death as the result of a wound in 1833. With regard to wolf-reared children, there is the example of two little girls, aged about eight and two respectively, who were picked up by a missionary at Midnapore in India while they were living in the midst of a pack of wolves and in perfect accord with them. This case, which is comparable to that of Mowgli, is the more plausible for happening in India, where the tamer wolves are more used to man, and it raises the problem of whether the two children were adopted by a she-wolf or abducted by one. Although the younger child died soon after rescue, the elder, named Kamala, survived for nine years. It took a very long time to tame her, for her life among wolves had made her as like them as possible. She ran at speed on all fours, gave voice to howls, preferred the company of wolves, at first spoke hardly at all, and showed no inclination to imitate; she shed but a tear or two at the death of her sister, and was void of emotion. It was extremely difficult to teach her to stand upright, to walk, to use her hands, and still harder to teach her to speak: she never spoke more than some fifty words. She lapped with her tongue, smelled out her food, explored by scent, had sharp night sight and very acute hearing; she was totally unable to laugh or smile. Thus a life that is not isolated, but spent in the company of animals, induces dehumanized behavior in man. This case attests to the child's power of imitation, and although the adaptation to a wolf's life was not perfect, it was nonetheless extraordinary when it is remembered how poorly the human anatomy is suited to it. The case certainly testifies to the effects of intelligence. The phenomenon is comparable to that of domesticated animals that become to some extent humanized, but their inability to learn a language does not allow as great a transformation. Nevertheless very different degrees of intelligence are shown by an isolated chimpanzee, one living in company with his congeners, and one living with man. It is difficult to form an opinion concerning Kamala's intelligence, since she was not given any objective tests, which alone would have let us know if her practical non-verbalized intelligence was, or was not, superior to that of a child who is unable to speak, or to that of a monkey. In any case, her intelligence could not have been gauged in comparison with normal human intelligence, since she was deprived of internal language, and therefore of true reflective thought.[2]

Nothing is known about Kamala's original aptitudes and it would be ridiculous to say, without reasons, that she was an idiot. Obviously it is not possible to segregate

[2] It would be necessary to know to what degree human thought lacking language can reach a level at which self-mastery is assured (consciousness of the selective ego).

an unweaned baby experimentally, but a case observed in America, and reported by K. Davis in 1940, has almost the value of an experiment: an illegitimate baby girl, who was entirely normal during the six months she spent in a crèche, was found tied up in a loft at the age of six. She was listless, had not learned to walk, and, never having had anything except milk, could only digest liquids. Upon being given care and attention, she started to smile and take notice. Tests made after six weeks showed a mental age of hardly one year, but after seven months she started to talk and to utter some sounds; then she could understand some things that were said to her, but could not talk. "It would have been most informative," Pieron tells us, "to have had details concerning her subsequent development.... Nevertheless, as regards this child who up to six months showed herself to be normal, it would appear that the subsequent isolation and segregation with no chance of exercise or of experimental play, together with the infliction of a barbarous animal life, have led to complete atrophies of the central structures."

## *Deaf Children*

Deaf children, and those who being both deaf and blind are deprived to an even greater extent, are also isolated subjects, but as a general rule they live in a society, whether it be normal society or the society of other deaf subjects. Although their infirmity deprives them of verbal motivation, they nevertheless retain the desire to communicate, living as they do in a social and cultural environment of which they strive to grasp something. They are therefore less deprived than truly isolated subjects.[3] It is difficult to form an exact opinion on the intelligence of deaf-mutes, since there are all the intermediary degrees between the totally uneducated deaf-mute, today a rarity, whose mental level will depend upon whether he is living alone, with hearing people, or with other deaf people; the deaf-mute trained to a gesture language that clumsily seeks to take the place of the verbal language; and, lastly, the deaf-mute who has been taught to speak normally, either from the outset or more or less slowly after having learned the gesture language. For another thing, many deaf people are not totally deprived of hearing, and their infirmity is only partial. Although deafness can, of course, afflict normal children, there are other cases in which it is accompanied by cerebral deficiencies. One thing is certain: apart from certain rare cases of cerebral lesions, deaf-mutes are only mute because they are deaf,[4] and their intelligence is only deficient to the extent that their thought processes do not make full use of the verbal tool that is the instrument of internal language. An adequate education in the techniques of speaking has enabled deaf-mutes, and even blind deaf-mutes, to reach high levels of culture. Indeed, nothing is more remarkable than the existence of these two facts

[3] In particular, the consciousness of the ego can be awakened in them in an elementary fashion even in the absence of language.

[4] Either from birth, or from any time before the age of seven, since, if language is not fixed firmly enough in the mind by usage, it will be forgotten if it is not heard.

side by side—the dependence of the human intelligence upon those sensory attributes that are the source of all cultural acquisitions, and the brain's extraordinary ability for substitution, which enables it, when deprived of the apparently indispensable sensory source, to succeed in building a normal intelligence in the absence of hearing, and even of both sight and hearing. The human brain's complexity makes it readily adaptable to the symbolisms of language and to the establishing of an internal language that is the source of reflective thought, irrespective of which senses are used for its education. Man in isolation can do nothing, but in society he can attain to human thought and culture by the most devious ways, by means of messages transmitted by his tactile and vibratory senses, for instance. Although in view of the social aspect of their life the dehumanization of deaf-mutes is less marked than that of man reared in isolation, and although they remain able to learn the techniques of speech for a longer time, it is nevertheless better to start training them as soon as possible—since, after all, they have no real barrier to articulation—and the ideal method is to start developing their speech at the babbling stage, which occurs in them as in normal babies. At the very latest they should begin to learn at about two and a half, whether by the help of any vestige of hearing left to them or by the use of substitutes for hearing, such as lip-reading and feeling the vibrations of the larynx by touch, something that is difficult, necessitating individual devotion, but essential, in which instruction by the mother is the only possible starting point. In these ways deaf subjects, taught to speak, come to possess a normal internal language, although one that comprises no auditory images.

The natural reaction of the deaf-mute who wants to communicate is to express himself in gestures, as a hearing person does in a foreign country;[5] the conventional deaf-and-dumb language, comprising a dactylologic alphabet that enables letters to be made with the fingers according to a particular code, is extremely ingenious and capable even of symbolizing elementary abstract conceptions, but it suffers from a grave disadvantage in that it lends itself badly to the language's higher forms: having a poor vocabulary, it lacks those potentialities of grammar that are so important for the developing of thought, and it cannot go beyond the stage of jargon, or pidgin language. "My father has given me an apple" becomes "Apple, father, me, give." Although the deaf-and-dumb language is capable of awakening human thought and reflection, it provides only an incomplete internal language and it creates unbreakable habits that will not disappear even after re-education in speech, which is why it is not used nowadays. It is an abnormal language, and one that is particularly difficult to align with language as written and read by properly instructed deaf-mutes.

The gesture is an ingenious substitution for language, but it is only capable of transmitting the cultural concept incompletely—it cannot get to the root of the matter; therefore it cannot originate the concept. The deaf-and-

[5] Spontaneous gesture language, unrelated to normal speech, is not the source of verbalized thought, and teachers with normal hearing only use it as a code into which they transpose their thoughts as a means of creating a genuine internal language.

dumb language, like writing, is always dependent upon the spoken language. The awakening of thought always aims at creating an internal language in the brain, more or less like that of the normal subject.

In order to learn more about the psychology of man without language, we should very much like to have the testimony of deaf-mutes as regards their mental state before they learned any language, either oral or by gestures, but when one thinks of how difficult it is for even a normal man to recall the state of mind he was in some years before, it is not surprising that it should be still harder for a deaf-mute, and none of us retain many memories of our babyhood before we could speak. A non-verbalized thought can only be badly expressed in words. The very paucity of the testimony is a proof of how important is the appearance of internal language to the thought process: it is the manifestation of a veritable revolution in human development. Nevertheless it must be stressed that this process of human development did not start from zero: the social man had already developed a certain degree of humanization, and his consciousness was more in evidence than that of man in isolation. It is most interesting to study the various types of deaf-mute with modern test methods, although—fortunately for the subjects, but unfortunately for science—it is nowadays no longer possible to find those extreme cases that would be the most interesting. Non-verbal tests on the deaf-mute simply show a backwardness in intellectual development that confirms the importance of language. The backwardness is more noticeable in exercises that demand a capacity for abstract thought.

Thus the study of a man with a normal brain, but deprived of the possibility of acquiring language, confirms the conclusions furnished by child, animal and comparative psychologies and psychophysiology: the human method of thought, which is only possible by reason of the number of neurons in man's brain, develops solely under the influence of language, which provides the human means of thought. Subjects deficient in the sensory faculties become normal human beings to the extent that they acquire language. Dehumanization is greater if social deprivation is more nearly complete. Just as it is extremely difficult for us to assess the potentialities of animal thought, so it is with man deprived of language. A man without speech is not truly a man, even though his practical ability to think in nonverbal images and his consciousness of self are superior to that of an animal. It is particularly interesting to compare the similarities that exist between infantile thought before full mastery of language is attained, certain traits of thought in deaf-mutes, various aspects of the human subconscious (Jung), notably in dreams, and the method of thought in primitive peoples at the stage of that *pre-verbal* thought, all of which differ from our adult civilized thought. Thus several facts go to prove that consciousness is still only very imperfectly established, and the reason for this can be put down to the inadequacies of language, to the lack of a satisfactory method of collective thought. Animism, totemism, belief in the reality of dreams, belief in the possibility of being in two places at once, and confusion between yesterday and tomorrow (the non-present) are some of the forms of pre-philosophic and pre-scientific thought that are encountered in legends and that still have not entirely vanished from some contemporary societies. The child and primitive man suffer when isolated from the world and from the formative and protective society. Genuine personal consciousness, allied to the development of language and reason,[6] is the entirely recent acquisition of a humanity that has taken more than half a million years to evolve. The concept of man as a free and responsible entity arose beside the Mediterranean's blue waves from the conjunction of Greek thought and Jewish thought, to which we are heirs. However, its affirmation of each individual's unique worth should not make us forget that the freedom of the individual could not be achieved apart from the human community, since it is the blossoming of a cultural process always moving toward unsuspected tomorrows, but that has now reached a crucial point with all humanity's cultural patterns unifying around a scientific and rational method of thought.

[6] Mankind's progress involves a progress of the language. Mathematics is a variety of language, and logic is founded upon the neurophysiology of the brain. Aesthetics makes use of other variants of language, notably music.

# 8 / The Insane

Psychiatry, which treats of changes in the human consciousness that make the subject unsuitable for social life, by describing the mentally sick as "alienated"—that is, as aliens to the normal—has first to deal with the problem of language, language expressed or thought. Mental disturbances are frequently revealed by speech disturbances. Since it is impossible to review all such manifestations, we shall limit ourselves to considering inadequacies of speech, leaving aside such matters as delirium, wrongful interpretations expressed in apparently normal language, and all cases of auditory hallucination in which the sufferer hears voices that influence him by affecting either his thoughts or his actions. Some cases of speech inadequacy represent the converse of those described in the last chapter, and relate not to the environment, but to a disturbance of the brain, which, in spite of normal social contacts and good hearing, evinces an inability to acquire speech at the normal age. Other cases, met with in the adult who has learned to speak, involve a state of insanity that bodily diminishes the cerebral function, thus differing from aphasia, which specifically attacks speech; and sufferers from this form of insanity must be distinguished from those subjects who, more or less voluntarily, refuse to speak and submerge themselves in silence. Lastly, and of a quite different nature, there is the true alienation of language frequently met with in dementia praecox, or schizophrenia, in which the sufferer invents a special language for himself that to a greater or lesser degree distorts either the vocabulary or syntax of normal language. Here what is remarkable is the brain's power of creating words, and this manifests itself in what, pathologically speaking, is a very unusual form: this creation of words does not operate *ex nihilo* since the subjects affected possessed normal speech before they became ill.

## *The Speech of Mental Defectives*

For a child to follow the normal course of linguistic evolution that will lead him to speech, it is not enough simply for him to live in a speaking environment, hearing spoken language. He must also have a brain whose development has taken place, and that normally. This development can be disturbed by a great many factors, and here we can do no more than mention some of the most important, such as hereditary factors that can involve either malformations of a genetic type present in the line of descent, even though the parents may not have manifested the chromosomic combinations producing them—these are especially significant where there is consanguinity—or factors that relate to the condition of the gametes themselves and to conditions affecting the life of the embryo and foetus, such as diseases of the mother, like syphilis (which may be less blameworthy than is sometimes thought), diabetes or German measles, and all these are especially dangerous for the embryo when its organs are being formed, since they can either affect the formation of the organs directly, or disturb the hormonal determinisms of the embryogenesis, while toxic agents, especially those devolving from alcoholism, can affect not only the gametes, but also the conditioning of the embryo by producing cerebral changes. Other causal factors still remain unknown, and these can produce unpleasant surprises in childbirth, such as hydrocephalus and Mongolism, of whose origins we are ignorant. Moreover, the embryo and the foetus can be directly afflicted without the mother showing any symptoms. Diseases that attack the nursing baby[1] and the young child can also produce disorders, either by affecting the growth and maturation of the organs themselves, or by impeding the child's contacts with the outside world. All these factors result in delays of development that afflict the child with a neuropsychological behavior pattern that is not appropriate to its true age, and the outcome is identical to that affecting isolated and deaf children. It is often difficult to distinguish between the deficiency that is due to the thought processes' forma-

[1] Frequently resulting from a difficult delivery.

tive environment, which may involve a lack of care and attention, and the deficiency that is due to an inherent cerebral disorder. Although theoretically the wolf-reared child is exceptional, he is retarded from the practical viewpoint of re-education. Above all, a distinction must be made between those children whose brains have serious anatomical defects[2] and those who simply have physiological disorders, that is, those whose cerebral defects have an extraneous cause such as a thyroid deficiency, which can perhaps be treated. The further back the disturbance goes in the embryonal life, the more pronounced are the lesions and insufficiencies of development, the harder is it to remedy the condition, and the longer the treatment takes. Every case offers different features, and classifications can only be made for convenience. Any backwardness in the child's essential behavior patterns, and especially that of language, should be brought to the attention of medical and psychological specialists, and tests should be carried out to evaluate the child's intelligence. For practical purposes, a distinction is made in mental backwardness between the profoundly deficient states, which are hardly amenable to education, such as *idiocy* and *imbecility,* and the states where improvement can be hoped for, such as *mental debility* and *simple retardation.*

Idiocy, or a mental age of zero up to two years, involves the gravest deficiency of intelligence, and there is a serious ineptitude for the acquisition of speech. "Any child," say Binet and Simon, "is an idiot who does not

[2] Although the mental possibilities of some sufferers from hydrocephalus with reduced brains are quite astonishing.

succeed in communicating with his fellows by speech; that is to say, who can neither express his thoughts verbally, nor understand thoughts expressed by others, assuming that this pseudo-aphasia is entirely due to intellectual deficiency and that there is nothing wrong with the child's hearing or with his phonatory organs."

Clearly, this intellectual deficiency is only the result of the brain's inability to develop the conditioned reflexes that form language's system of signals. Some idiots are capable of repeating numerous words parrot-fashion. The lack of intelligence is accompanied by various physical malformations signs of degeneration, and by backwardness in every sphere, including the growing of teeth and gait. The degree of idiocy varies from absolute zero to the demonstration of some emotion and an ability to learn his name. The idiot will invariably be unable to take care of himself.

The imbecile has a mental age ranging from two to six years. He is classically defined by his inability to learn to read and write, and he has a much more normal appearance than the idiot. His incapacity for abstract thought is in contrast to his good memory, which can provide him with certain talents, and there are some well-known instances of imbeciles who were adept at calculation. Mental defectives, often characterized as simpletons, have a mental age ranging from seven to twelve years, and sometimes there are affective disorders and sometimes not. Lastly, and above them, there are the individuals who are simply intellectually retarded, and these can be prognosticated more easily. True mental deficiency must not be confused with false retardation, which can be due to laziness, distraction, timidity or childishness. Unlike the idiots, who are incapable of leading an independent existence, and the mentally retarded, who can be trained, the imbeciles and the mental defectives are faced, above all, with problems of social integration and, the prey of every vice and temptation, they compose the majority of delinquents and misfits.

The various mental disorders all demonstrate the extent to which a mastery of the psychological being is linked to the possession of an internal language, but without dwelling on this we shall describe some disorders of linguistic expression that are especially worthy of attention, and that concern, to a greater or lesser degree, the three attributes of speech—its articular realization, its function as the regulator of understanding, and its appetitive function of the desire to speak. The development of speech can be inhibited by an emotional complex evincing symptomatic dumbness. The speech impediments that are encountered most frequently are *stammering* and defects in articulation such as *lisping* that involve changes in the pronunciation of the consonants and confusion of the vowel sounds, whether due to malformations of the phonatory structure or to a functional defect of the brain. To these must be added impediments affecting reading and writing: *dyslexia* and *dysorthographia,* involving confusion between letters that are similar in shape or sound and the transposition of letters, i. e. *Spoonerism.* A whole pathology of speech exists, which, when it is properly understood, will be of the highest interest in connection with cerebral physiology. The importance of these defects, and the possibilities of their correction, depend upon the entire cerebral context. The impediments of understanding are more serious than those of execution, and the correction of writing should only be undertaken after that of articulation. "Every child of normal intelligence who is backward in speech after the age of four ought to have special training, otherwise there will subsequently be a risk of stammering, and in any case, he will not be able to learn to write in the years that follow."

Alongside these cases in which an inherent mental deficiency prevents the adult from having a normal psychology at his command, since, due to his cerebral inadequacy as a child, he has not been able to construct the mechanisms of the internal language, must be placed those cases in which a normal individual with a normal psychology and an internal language sinks into a state of dementia following an injury to the brain of one sort or another; this is essentially a *mental deterioration.* Mental backwardness and dementia finally result in the same type of deficiency, although they attain it by different routes. However, in dementia, which affects an already formed psychology, the linguistic aspect is less important. "The regression of the demented subject is characterized by the fact that he displays the remnants of former acquisitions: certain words of his vocabulary, certain memories, certain mannerisms exist, which are of major diagnostic importance." Moreover, in dementia, the deterioration affects all the mental functions, such as the memory and the attention, and not just the judgment, as with those who are inherently afflicted. The deterioration of dementia is defined as "a defect in the psychological synthesis that leads to mental impotence in the sufferer." The regression toward a primitive stage of behavior is characterized by an anarchistic freeing of automatisms and actions of instinctive and affective origin. The demented subject, established in his dementia, has a mutilated personality. The euphoric dementia of General Paralysis of the Insane and the various forms of senile dementia are especially characteristic of mental deterioration. In G.P.I., which is a manifestation of syphilis of the nervous system, speech disorders are particularly noticeable owing to the trembling of the phonatory muscles, and the following traits are much in evidence: hesitation, slow enunciation, stumbling over sounds, altered words, which are clearly revealed in the repetition of difficult test words, such as "anti-constitutionally." Numerous linguistic alterations of a similar kind can be added to these and the disease also affects writing, inducing tremblings of the hand and forgetfulness of words and letters, and providing in every way a picture comparable to that of speech.

## *The Alienation of Language*

*Schizophrenia* is a psychopathological state akin to that of dementia—indeed, it was formerly called dementia praecox—and it is characterized by serious symptomatic disorders that, however, do not lead to melancholic depression or to maniacal excitement, but to a sort of detachment from the outside world: the patient retreats into himself and lives in a world of his own that is quite incomprehensible to the healthy mind *(autism).* Instead of a suppression of values, as in dementia, there is a transposition of values: the subject is truly alienated, that is, estranged. Since language is the factor of relationship and communication, binding man to his fellow men, it is not surprising that in schizophrenia it should be disturbed, not in the articulation, but in its very symbolic essence, its significance; to a lesser degree, alienation of language is found in other psychopathic states. The schizophrenic attempts to create for himself a *new* language, and this language presents creative aspects as well as deficient ones. It is characterized by severe grammatical and syntactical changes, such as are found in telegraphese and pidgin-language; there can be strings of words without syntax, ellipses omitting the phrase's essential element and disruption of normal word order: "Twenty-one years, born the Paris 16e, no brothers, I have some sons, twenty-fifth of March" instead of: "Twenty-one years old, I was born on March 25 in Paris 16e and I have no brothers, I only have some sons." Thus schizophrenia results in a degree of verbal incoherence that involves the transformation of words, either by replacing one word with another, or by transposing syllables, often by association; this is termed *schizophasia,* and is evident in the written language as well. In this earliest stage of the disorder, the language is alienated from the thoughts it wants to express, and at a later stage "it is the language's function itself that is alienated. Speech appears to have lost its function of communication. . . . The speech mechanisms go through the motions, but no verbal fabric results."

The forms taken by this purposeless pouring out of words are various—some contain philological associations ("the hand, *die Hand,* five, it is October 5, St. Joseph's hand has been cut off"), others comprise whole series of assonant words, or labored puns are dragged into inappropriate contexts, or words repeated with an echo effect, or the recurring of particular phrases and word patterns, or nonsensical rigmaroles endlessly recited.

Even stranger, by reason of their expressiveness and originality, are the "private" languages made up of incomprehensible neologisms invented by schizophrenics, and these launch out into curious displays of the imagination, bearing symbolisms analogous to those of dreams, endowing words with new meanings and creating new forms of grammar and syntax that can be most interesting: letters are added or subtracted, two words can be fused to form one, such as "miserocious" (formed from "miserable" and "ferocious"), they can be more complex still: these fruits of the delirious thoughts they strive to express can be either interpreted by the normal mind, or entirely incomprehensible. Sometimes a schizophrenic will succeed in constructing a genuine language that, in its form, differs little from certain types of slang, and this may be achieved by the systematic suppression of particular letters or by the addition of groups of letters to every word spoken, written or read. Parallel with forms of language that have meaning for the sufferer, there may be other forms, such as are met with in *glossomania,* that are devoid of meaning and involve simply a verbal game played with new words and without any attempt at syntax. A perfection rarely attained is encountered in *glossolalia,* and this involves the invention of an entirely new language, by means of which the schizophrenic expresses his thought and to which he gives a special name. Alienated language can also develop a particular style, which may be evasive, emphatic or eccentric according to the way in which the mind is affected. In schizophrenic language, semantics and syntax are sacrificed to rhythm and the phonetic pattern, and sometimes a poetic result emerges that cannot fail to recall the poetry of the Surrealists, such as this Mallarmian example quoted by Quercy:

*Sans erreur on sourit envisageant la source*
*Etincelant abri des prolixes émaux*
*Parce que, doute pur, entraine, selon course*
*Intérimaire pli chez mystiques arceaux.*

(You smile without delusion envisaging the source
Scintillating haven of enamels diffuse
Since simple doubt leads on according to the course
Enfolded in the interim archways so abstruse.)

Paintings by schizophrenics are equally surrealistic, and this raises the eternal question of the relationship between art and madness. An authentic artist can be alienated, but on the whole he can assume the state of alienation *voluntarily.* As well as the artist who is peacefully content to be traditional there is the questing experimenter who, feeling that normal language and representational drawing leave a part of reality unexpressed, seeks the missing element. To search for a more comprehensive language is certainly legitimate, and it is not surprising that there should be common ground between the normal individual who constructs such a language creatively and the alienated individual who, also rejecting normal language, evolves a new one as the expression of an automatic process, especially since in both cases the subconscious will play a preponderant part. The normal and the pathological are not irreducibly separated. A normal subject discovers in the depths of his being, beneath the cultural veneers of language, patterns of thought connecting him to the savage, and these are not so very different from those displayed by the disordered brain of a schizophrenic. It is the non-mastery of his trouble, and the non-consciousness of his state, that characterize the schizophrenic.

Since the neurophysiology of language as an instrument of thought, like all the physiology of the cerebral cortex, is still poorly understood in spite of constant and remarkable progress, it is not surprising that it should be the same as regards physiopathology. For a long time neurologists have known about the localized lesions of the brain that lead to some particular disorders; as regards the more comprehensive disorders that are the subject of psychiatry, we now know that they mostly arise, not from local lesions, but from disturbances of the functioning of the whole cerebral cortex, but we know little of how they come about. A time will come when physiology will profit from the study of certain alienations of language —just as it has been able to utilize the hysterical manifestations—to acquire a better understanding of the thought process and the cerebral function as a whole. But that time is still far off. Today we only know that an important part must be played in disorders by the regulating centers of the brain's connective system, which is the source of the psychiatric manifestations. It is by acting upon those centers that shock therapy, involving dissolution and reconstruction of the functional neuronic structure (Delmas-Marsalet), sometimes effects cures, as Delay, in particular, has demonstrated. The serious surgical operations in which the prefrontal regions are suppressed or disconnected from the centers at the base of the brain have also had a certain efficacy, but so far nothing more is known of what really causes a normal individual, with a controlled character, to become a schizophrenic foundering in alienation.

Sometimes there is a certain similarity between the speech of schizophrenics and that of aphasiacs, but in fact the two disorders have nothing in common: aphasiacs hesitate and trip over their words, but schizophrenics find in their language "a new way of existing in the world."

In spite of the strangely exalted character of certain manifestations of alienated language and their relationship with some of the highest forms of human thought, the creative power of the alienated subject is nonetheless relatively diminished. Whereas the surrealist writer succeeds by reason of his mastery over language, the schizophrenic is characterized by his inability to master everyday language, and, indeed, it masters him: "I lost myself in the sense of the words" said one patient, and alienated language is, above all, a reduction or "a sharp lowering in the individual or cultural scale of the levels reached by philological evolution." Although schizophrenia is of great interest as demonstrating the mind's creative power as regards words, it does not confront us with a productive process on the part of the mind in any cultural or individual sense, since it has lost its essential function, which is communication. "It is the aim of psychiatry," Racamier tells us, "having identified the mental disorder through the altered forms of speech that express and betray it, to lead the patient, again by means of language, back into the world from which he is estranged."

# 9 / *Aphasiacs and Stammerers*

Besides the psychiatric disorders that affect the main psychological functions and only concern the pathology of speech because human psychology expresses itself in words, there are other disturbances that influence speech more directly since they devolve from cerebral lesions at the level of the speech centers. These disorders, which bear to a greater or lesser degree on both aspects of speech, the internal as well as the external, disturb the functioning of the mind, but in a less general way than is found in the psychopathies; these are the *aphasias* comprising loss of speech due to brain injury; following the artificial dichotomy applied to human knowledge, they come under neurology. *Stammering* is included in this study of the aphasias since, although it is apparently a purely articular disturbance, it in fact betrays disorders in the functioning of the speech centers in the neighborhood of those that are responsible for the aphasic suppressions and, thus, it has considerable importance for the psychophysiology of speech and thought.

## *The Aphasias*

It has been known for a long time that some disorders, above all the vascular ones that prevent the functioning of certain parts of the brain, lead to a selective suppression of speech. The conception of the speech centers as expounded in our previous chapters emerges from the discoveries of various leading anatomopathologists, first among whom was Paul Broca, who in 1861 described precisely the motor center of speech in the left frontal area. Then, in 1874, attention was drawn to the gnosic aspect of language by Wernicke, who identified the temporal auditory center as the source of verbal deafness, and showed that various associative patterns were accounted for by lesions among the centers responsible for imagery, and then these distinctions were found also to apply to the act of writing. Present-day ideas concerning the aphasias originated with P. Marie (1906), who showed the importance of loss of the internal language in aphasia and established that the effects of the lesions were far more extensive than had been realized; he distinguished two types of aphasia, according to whether loss of the internal language was accompanied by anarthria or not. The first type is *Wernicke's aphasia,* in which the patient has articulated language but speaks badly because he lacks vocabulary, syntax, etc.; the second type is *Broca's aphasia* (similar to the preceding, but complicated by anarthria), in which the patient is mute or almost so. Simple loss of articular control, or anarthria, with no disturbance of the internal language, is not true aphasia. In 1926, Head was able to identify several gradations of aphasia, according to whether it was the word structure that was lost, its usage, grammatical relationships or the general sense of the conversation. Some time before that, Jackson had stressed the relationship existing between speech disorders and disorders of motor control discernible at several levels of function; and this distinction between affective automatic speech and voluntary intellectual speech has recently been taken up again by Alajouanine to throw new light on the problem of aphasia. He maintains that neither the word nor the phrase is the basic element of speech, since they result from a subordinate grammatical analysis; we think by means of acquired formulas, "ready-made expressions that evoke and suggest each other" in an automatic flow that thought hardly controls. We learn these expressions in childhood, and it is only subsequently that we learn to separate them into words and to analyze them grammatically. The child who expresses himself well is still unable to write correctly: he does not separate the words as written, and he does not distinguish between homonyms. "In contrast to these automatic formulas are the constructions of voluntary speech: they take over when the speaker switches from everyday speech to less habitual speech in order to explain something difficult, and particularly when he embarks upon long and complicated phrases. . . . Then the building up of the phrase becomes a voluntary act and a genuine construction.... An integral property of normal language is precisely its power to switch continuously from ready-made phrases to constructed ones, from automatic speech to voluntary speech," which Jackson called "standard speech and made-up speech;" and it is the power of choice between them that is disturbed in aphasia, in which automatic speech shows itself as being far more durable than voluntary speech.

Localized disorders are rare that produce only verbal blindness, verbal deafness or an anarthria with no disturbance of the internal language. Disorders that attack the zone of language lying between the parietal, occipital, temporal and frontal areas affect collectively the conditioned reflexes that insure the verbalization of thought, whether or not verbalization is disturbed. Every case of aphasia necessitates an exact and detailed study that will alone indicate at what level the disturbances are seated and, in particular, whether they relate simply to reception and execution, or whether they also involve the intelligence. Spontaneous speech must be studied for disorders of articulation, vocabulary and syntax, and the speech must be repeated interminably if the patient cannot make himself understood. The aphasiac often shows a total forgetfulness of vocabulary, and upon recognizing an object to which he is unable to give a name, offers various substitutions for it, and may repeat one word endlessly irrespective of whether it is suitable (word intoxication). Sometimes speech is limited to the uttering of oaths and swearwords; a song, or sometimes just its tune, can persist after speech has been lost. The comprehension of speech is studied by having the patient carry out orders that become more and more complicated: for example, P. Marie's test with three pieces of paper—the first is to be put in the pocket, the second given back and the third torn up. Verbal deafness prevents all comprehension, but, on the other hand, an aphasiac unable to pronounce a word can retain total comprehension. Finally, the patient's attitude to reading and writing must be examined. There are degrees in alexia, loss of the ability to read: it may show itself as an inability to recognize which way around or which way up the text should be read, or as a non-recognition of certain letters and known words, or as failure to understand the text read aloud and to retain it. Similarly agraphia, loss of the ability to write, can vary according to whether the matter is written spontaneously, dictated or copied; and the spelling out of words with lettered blocks, which does not need accurate control of the hand, can also be disturbed; here a distinction must be made between agraphia and ordinary apraxia. Mimicry and gestures must be studied: a patient who can make a simple gesture may be incapable of a complex gesture—he will strike the candle on the matchbox and not the match. When it is purely verbal images that are affected, the recognition of noises, shapes and colors can persist. Calculation, telling the time and drawing are also to be taken into consideration, since there are conditions of *acalculia* (inability to calculate) as well as *amusia* (inability to recognize or reproduce tone). The ability to read is more durable than the ability to write. In all these conditions, everything that pertains to automatism, such as the patient's ability to give his name and address, is retained the longest.

Alajouanine separates the syndrome[1] of the speech disturbances into three elements: (1) disturbance of voluntary evocation of vocabulary; (2) disturbance of the syntactical construction of the phrase; and (3) inability to envisage words collectively. The word that cannot be evoked voluntarily will appear spontaneously when a ready-made phrase is uttered as the result of an emotional shock, or if the patient quotes a proverb. A mother may be unable to speak the name of her daughter, and yet, in a fit of crying, will cry out "Poor Jacqueline, I no longer know how to speak your name!" A patient may be unable to put a name to a hare when he sees one, yet, in answer to the question "Running like what?" he may reply "Like a hare." The disability varies according to the intensity of the aphasia, and in slight cases it will be groups of complex phrases that cannot be evoked. In more serious cases syntax will be affected, and in the gravest cases of all it is the vocabulary that is lost. The most recent acquisitions of language disappear first, but during re-education of the aphasiac, progression is in the opposite direction. "If aphasia restrains thought as seriously as action, this is not at all because the aphasiac no longer knows how to speak or read or write correctly. It is because he is quite as seriously incapacitated as a deaf-mute or a blind man, and his whole thought process is falsified by a disorder that limits vocabulary and syntax to the extent of paralyzing all mental formulation." The speech and thought of the

[1] He calls it *le syndrome de dissociation automatico-volontaire.*

aphasiac are weighed down by an extraordinary sluggishness.

According to Alajouanine, Wernicke's aphasia is characterized by this disassociation between automatic speech, which persists, and voluntary speech, which disappears, without articular disturbance, and Broca's aphasia includes some types in which, in addition to articular disturbances that cause articulation to regress to an infantile stage, there is a total disappearance of speech, automatic as well as voluntary: the sufferer says only one word, or perhaps a few words that are always the same.

What differentiates aphasia from psychiatric disorders and, in particular, from the states of dementia lies in the fact that in aphasia the main intellectual functions are only affected to the extent that they are verbalized. Factual memory is retained, and non-verbal tests disclose a normal state as regards attention, imagination and judgement. On the whole, aphasiacs are quite able to take notice of their state, of which they are fully conscious and from which, unable to communicate their thought, they suffer a great deal. They are perfectly at ease with the concrete, but the abstract gives them much more difficulty, since they have retained thought by means of images and have lost formulated thought. An aphasiac is crippled as regards his thought because he has lost the use of language, and this emphasizes once more the relationship between human thought and speech. The aphasiac who loses the power of speech loses more than a means of expression. His thought process itself is disturbed, since it is verbalized, but he is neither a demented person—whose cerebral functions are all deficient, even those that are non-verbalized—nor an isolated child who has not learned to speak. The individual who has not known language can never raise himself to the level of a truly human form of thought and consciousness. The individual who, thanks to language, has once reached that level—as long as his brain has not given way completely, and if he is simply deprived of thought as regards its verbalized functioning—retains a human method of thinking and reflecting by means of thought, using non-verbal images. Frequently he retains automatic speech, but even if he is deprived of that and can say neither "I" nor his name, he still retains a conscious conception of his ego, and the reflective detachment he acquired as a child by means of language. The primary system of signals remains human, even if the secondary system has disappeared[2] but at a time when he had already been humanized. Since language is the human brain's invention for social communication, he who is deprived of social relations at the outset does not become human, but he who like the deaf-man remains in a social environment, or he who like the aphasiac has been socialized in humanity, can never be as completely dehumanized as man in isolation.

Although the total aphasiac is not amenable to reeducation, the aphasiac on the other hand who has retained part of his automatic speech may laboriously regain a degree of voluntary control; the best way to help him is to build upon what remains to him; and young subjects

[2] Most frequently the aphasiac loses the ability to express himself and to evoke his thoughts in a verbalized way, rather than losing his automatic language—man's means of thought—which persists subconsciously.

are easier to re-educate. To psychological reinstruction in the internal language—effected by learning words, syntactical construction, texts that have to be completed, formulae, etc.—must be added where necessary the phonetic re-education of articulation. The lesions of the dominant hemisphere in which the aphasia lies are the sole causes of the speech disturbances, and it is in that hemisphere alone that re-education takes place.[3] It is not possible to substitute for the damaged hemisphere the uninjured one. On the other hand, as regards hemiplegia in children, the unaffected hemisphere becomes capable of learning normal speech even after suppression of the dominant hemisphere.

## *Stammering*

Stammering appears as a particular disorder of articulation: there may be convulsive repetition of one or more phonemes, the introduction of a superfluous phoneme to facilitate speech, or a transitory check during which the mouth opens but no sounds are uttered. It is accompanied by disturbances of the respiratory rhythm, unnecessary movements of the tongue, lips and face, and vasomotor irregularities involving intense emotion. Thus it is possible to relate stammering to anarthria, and to consider it solely as a disturbance of the motor system of speech, but in fact the problem is far more complex, since on the one hand stammering is often a neurosis, and on the other it is accompanied by actual disturbances of the thought process

[3] The case of left-handed people is dealt with below.

and of the internal language: it is not that the stammerer is unable to pronounce particular words, but that he cannot effectively think of them, and fills the gap by repeating a phoneme that at least is available. The pathogenesis of stammering is still far from being fully elucidated, and it is likely that there are several different types. According to Garde, for instance, there is a type of stammering that has a purely motor origin, as well as an aphasic type that is related to different centers.

Stammerers are always the subjects of a particular emotional state and stammering is frequently associated with various psychosomatic disturbances. Thus in view of the importance of the centers at the base of the brain as regards emotion it has been thought (Seeman) that the motor disturbance of stuttering is to be found at the level of the automatic motor centers of the *corpus striatum*. Furthermore, in view of the important relationships existing between the cortex and the centers of the cerebral base, this does not eliminate the possibility of intervention by the cortical phonative centers: in the course of operations in neural surgery, it has been possible to obtain the repetition of a phoneme by exciting the supplementary frontal speech center in a normal subject. Stammering is extremely variable according to circumstances and is particularly evident when the subject is intimidated or tired.

According to studies made by Pichon and Borel-Maisonny, disturbances of an aphasic type are always found in stammerers: difficulty in evoking words, troubles with syntax and narration, and defects in the cadence of sentences. These authorities maintain that stammerers are subjects in whom verbal thought has not developed normally to take precedence over thought by means of images and thus, in Pavlovian terms, the primary system has remained preponderant. The effort of conveying the images verbally hinders the words from presenting themselves at the desired moment; and stammerers are often intelligent children who have been backward as regards speech. The fact that highly intelligent subjects can be afflicted with this infirmity, although it does not dismiss the existence of sufferers to whom the above explanation is applicable, suggests that it is perhaps not the only explanation, and is an argument in favor of there being several types of stammering.

In the pathogenesis of stammering, the importance of *frustrated left-handedness* has been greatly stressed (Kovarski). Left-handed subjects have their speech centers located in the right hemisphere and this offers no particular inconvenience. As regards writing, they may have a tendency to produce mirror-writing, but in general it is easy for them to adapt themselves to normal usages. However, if right-handed parents or teachers compel them, out of prejudice, to use their right hand, the resulting frustration leads in quite a large number of cases to a variety of disorders, such as neurotic manifestations, psychosomatic disturbances and, in particular, stammering. Indeed, the functioning of the brain finds itself subjected to imperfect conditions, since normally the control needed by such delicate and acquired operations as speech and writing should be exercised by only one hemisphere, the dominant one. If the left hemisphere is forced to learn the process of writing after the right hemisphere has learned the process of speech, the result can be serious disorders of cerebral coordination, and control is apt to be poor. Actually, the aphasias of left-handed subjects often result from lesions in both hemispheres, the dominant one as well as in the one they have been taught to use by their right-handed mentors. More often than not this involves no inconvenience, but it is not always so. Thus it is advisable to diagnose left-handedness as early on as possible, and then not to frustrate it, although not all the authorities are in agreement on the importance of this factor.

Nevertheless it appears to be confirmed by observations made in the auditory sphere. B. S. Lee was able to induce an experimental stammer in a normal subject by having him listen through earphones to his own voice slightly retarded. According to Tomatis, each of us has a dominant ear. In left-handed stammerers it is the left ear that is weaker, and in right-handed stammerers the right, while the opposite is true of normal individuals. By neutralizing a normal subject's better ear some of the phenomena of stammering can be induced in him. It is possible to cure stammerers rapidly by making dominant whichever ear would normally be so. Thus, again, it is conflict between the two cerebral hemispheres that produces disturbances of elocution, but this is not the place to go into the various psychotherapeutic, linguistic and neurological aspects of the therapeutics of stammering.

## *Conclusions*

Intelligence, thought, conscience, these familiar words that strive to express the very essence of our being, this mastery and power, this ability for looking inward that leads to the dualism that separates the soul from the body, appear compact of ambiguity. They seem to suggest an innate endowment, an ability of the human mind of which we are so proud when we compare ourselves with the animals. Yet it is not this aptitude of the human adult that is wonderful so much as the fact that at the outset there was nothing of it. We forget that newborn entity, totally lacking all psychological activity, which was, nevertheless, ourself, and which, in fact, was not really new: the true beginning was that inert egg, remote from the external world, and infinitely less intelligent than the lowliest amoeba, ruling its daily life by the mastery of its tropisms. Then our mind was nonexistent, except as regards potentiality. Because that egg is formed of living human matter[1] it is destined, after innumerable divisions, to provide above all this amazing brain, itself able to act creatively on the basis of activating messages reaching it through senses, thought and consciousness. We are human beings, and among our human organs we have a brain more complex than any other, yet this brain will be useless to us unless it is brought into action, unless it is put to work; this never-ending work is the genesis of the mind, beginning in the subconscious and the anonymity of the lower automatisms, and striving gradually toward the consciousness that will allow the formation of a personal and attainment of consciousness, which enables the formation to become individual and designed; the intelligence, the mind and the reflective consciousness are created by biological growth in the midst of the environment, and their assumption of control is only secondary to this. Without forgetting that original endowment of possibilities contained in the egg's substance, it can be said that at the outset we do not think because we are intelligent, but we become intelligent and capable of thought due to the progress of the brain's functioning. Everything depends upon the interaction between living matter and the environment. "Knowledge," wrote Lenin, "is the reflection of nature by man. Yet it is not a simple reflection, instantaneous and total; this process consists of a whole series of abstractions, formulations, laws and the formation of concepts. . . ."

[1] In regard to the essential characteristics of this matter, we still know nothing insofar as they pertain to the means by which the differentiation of the species was organized in the course of the highly complex processes of evolution.

Among these abstractions is to be found the distinction between the person and the environment, and this implies the ego capable of judgment.

Yet for all that, the nature alone is not enough. There must be society, culture and its long historical progression. Strictly speaking, it was not society that created man; man is the product of a mutation forming the culminating point of the complex processes incurred by biological evolution, and we are still almost entirely ignorant of the processes on which this phenomenon is based; nor do we know why, as the Tertiary period was ending, the multiple chance fluctuations of these specific forms culminated in the human form, with its greater brain. Man, in his original state, found what every human child still receives: that is, everything and yet nothing, an infinite possibility and an aptitude for intelligence and consciousness far exceeding an animal's, but an aptitude only, a sort of gigantic calculating machine that is nothing unless utilized, a brain whose wealth of neurons permits infinite new potentialities both in the sphere of the conditioned reflexes and in that of psychological integration. The present-day newly born child acquires the human cerebral function and intelligence simply because his brain develops in a human environment charged with the history of civilization and culture, and from the outset he is confronted by all that humanity has acquired. Of course, everything was far more complicated for the original man, since then there was no accumulation of knowledge, there was no culture, there was no truly human environment and, indeed, there was nothing except small, primitive communities formed by a being whose intelligence gave him an aptitude for the solving of practical problems, for the use of tools, and for work; he was a sort of superior ape, who felt the need to communicate with his fellows, in a near-animal language that was more a means of securing common action than transmission of thought. No one can say just what degrees of thought, consciousness and intellectual mastery were attained by this man, who was completely a man as regards his brain, but one deprived of true speech, that is, of a cultural language.[2] Innumerable generations and the efforts of many individuals of genius were needed to transform this remarkable power of articular coordination—an innate property of the human brain and one possessed by every child, even when deprived of human contact—into a true language to create both a means of expression and a means of thinking. In this development of man's natural attributes, which was achieved by man himself in the course of the centuries as he became progressively more conscious and attained ever-higher degrees of cultivation, language was an invention of genius and one that did not come about by itself since no conception of it is entertained by children who lack human contact. Certainly man can think without lan-

[2] It is necessary, also, to make a distinction between Neanderthal man and the human forerunners of *Homo sapiens.* Primitive man can only be envisaged objectively by making a synthesis of the aspects of the Adam of science and the traditional Adam of faith, which are only apparently contradictory: this synthesis presents a being fully human as regards his aptitude for judgment and liberty of action, thanks to his superior brain, yet nonetheless one with a serious cultural disadvantage. At one and the same time he was both very near to us and very far from us.

guage, but he will not be capable of purely abstract thought without a material foundation, thought with no verbal image, such as idealist psychologists formerly spoke about, basing their theories on the automatic functioning of the thought process, even when we are not conscious of it. An animal thinks to the extent of its cerebral potentialities, and a man deprived of speech by natural means thinks, but this thought can be nothing but superior to that of the animal because his brain is more developed; he thinks by associating non-verbal images, the process that Pavlov calls the primary system of signals, which, common to both animal and man, is more powerful in the man. Even when man has language he retains this system of thought, which preponderates in dreams and with certain human types, but on the whole it is true to say that the primary system will be superseded by the existence of the secondary system of speech, which has developed the cerebral function. As yet we do not know exactly what degree of intelligence and reflective consciousness is possible in the absence of speech. The inadequacy of our means of intellectual communication with creatures that lack speech —that is to say, the difficulty of learning about animal psychology solely by means of animal behavior—and the inadequacy of applied tests, and the impossibility of making experiments by isolating a child, all compel us to rely upon those few cases we have of human beings deprived of speech, cases that are not of equal value: wolf-reared children,[3] dehumanized segregated subjects and deaf-

[3] These are particularly important since their ability to live in animal society by means of prolonged animal imitation speaks in favor of their intellectual qualities.

mutes who have not been re-educated, although living in a human society that influences them indirectly, and who are capable of spontaneously inventing a gesture language that allows some degree of practical intelligence to develop. This degree of intelligence is rapidly increased when an instructor imposes verbal language on it, thus providing the subject with a genuine internal language, but, since it is still linked to gestures, it will still be defective due to the lack of abstraction. Less useful is the evidence provided by the idiot since his brain is incapable of language anyway, or by the aphasiac whose secondary system of signals is always more or less affected: his voluntary thought often has to make use of the primary system, which is also sometimes impaired (agnosia) without his intelligence necessarily suffering, but since he has previously been able to speak, some traces of language will remain, so that he cannot be compared to a primitive man. We shall probably never know very exactly just what is the degree of internal mastery attained either by a superior animal or by a man without language, but we should not put it too low since the power of abstraction and generalization precedes language, but neither should we put it too high since this power cannot be really displayed except by means of language. In the course of a child's normal development the acquisition of sensorimotor control, the development of the intelligence, and learning to speak advance together; for the child to be able to learn the pronouns, he must distinguish between the outside world and himself; but the possession of the pronouns assures a more clearly defined distinction. It is when the child starts to speak that he distinguishes himself from the monkey; this demonstrates no more than a difference in the brain and the appearance of new possibilities for association, generalization and abstraction, allowing the development of language, without which the progress would be insignificant. Proud of our ability to think, we see in language no more than a means of expressing our thoughts, and certainly this language is the creation of human intelligence, but if human intelligence has been able to develop, if it blossoms afresh in each child, if we are truly men and not super-monkeys, if we are civilized, capable of abstract thoughts, of writing, of calculation, of science, if we decide our actions, if we have formulated ideals, and an expanding moral conscience rather than obscure feeling, if, in a word, we think, it is to language that we owe it. The highest form of thought is closely tied to language, and discloses itself to us as internal language: our verbalized cerebral function can detach itself from action; and it is not possible for a civilized man to think normally without language. All that we have encountered in the course of this book has provided proof of this, whether we were concerned with the differences between animal language and human language, with the mechanisms of verbalization that make use of the ordinary processes of cerebral physiology to achieve new ends, or, lastly, with various disorders, those that carry speech defects into the thought process, those that militate against the forming of the thought process in the child, and those that impair it in the mental diseases.

Thus man has learned to think by means of language.

He was able to use his intelligence to invent this language and then found in it a means of developing himself ever more fully; based on practical knowledge of nature, he has been able to establish an entirely fresh process comprising theoretical knowledge and full consciousness of self. Man's potentiality for freedom increases by the extent that he moves away from his animal state, and man, although closely akin to animals, seems suddenly as a result of language to belong to another order. Nevertheless it must be recognized that from the outset this difference was implicit in the potentialities of man's brain, the largest in nature: neither a monkey nor a parrot could invent a true language.

In the course of this work we have kept to the psycho-physiological plane, avoiding all metaphysics. Nevertheless, by showing how we become conscious of ourselves and of the world by means of language, and how our minds are deprived by the absence of language, we are in perfect agreement with the "materialist theory of knowledge" in its present-day form as professed, in particular, by dialectical materialism. If scientific progress has necessitated the renouncing of certain pre-scientific formulations of spiritual dualism, together with certain purely verbal explanations, it has also induced the materialists to a remarkable effort in the direction of the real. We have seen how it was the study of the physiology of speech in the framework of Pavlovian thought that led the Soviet psychologists to understand, in agreement with the prophetic views of Marx and Engels, and contrary to the errors of the mechanistic materialists, all the inherent particularities of psychology and human consciousness. Scientific realism impels spiritualism to become more materialist, and materialism to largely accept the classic views of spiritualism, in a movement of remarkable convergence. Yet, this convergence on the plane of material facts certainly does not involve metaphysical agreement. Like all other human terms, the word "materialism" is ambiguous: there is an accepted materialism that bases its understanding of the universal laws, whether pertaining to mind or matter, on science, and this materialism maintains that the human mind's specific characteristics originate in properties peculiar to the human brain, but an acceptance of this materialism does not mean that it must also be accepted on the metaphysical plane, on this plane there are two possible concepts of the world: one is the classical spiritualist concept, and the other maintains that everything is composed of matter in a state of perpetual evolution, that matter alone gives birth to the mind and that death results in the total disappearance of the human individual. The scientific viewpoint must take a neutral attitude to the problem, but true neutrality, giving rise to free will and open-mindedness, requires it to be shown that science in itself imposes nothing. The materialist hypothesis is credible, but the spiritualist hypothesis is just as credible, and it is enough to understand that on the scientific plane it can be in complete agreement with materialism. The act of Creation is not limited to any one single moment,[4] but implies that everything is always subject to a God who

[4] An eternal world will be no less a created world than the temporal one.

is not separate from His work but who is eternally present in it in an immanent fashion, and this without ceasing to be a personal and transcendent deity, and when the believer fully understands this he will never again be troubled by any materialist statement other than a denial of God's existence, and of this no compelling proof is possible. What, for the believer, are all the laws of nature if not the act of Creation taking place in evolution, and what is the forming of human consciousness in the individual's evolution if not the developing of a soul that is not separate from the body, but forms an indivisible unity with it, symbolized by the image of form and matter dear to Schoolmen? The soul is not an attribute of the mind. It is the very core of the individual, and it is already present at the formation of the egg, complete with its potentialities, which environment will in due course react upon; if the egg's physiochemical structure is the structure of a human individual, might not its metaphysical aspect be the soul? Man's most complex structure is an aspect of his soul's greatest complexity; if everything is within God, absolutely nothing on the scientific plane denies the possibility of survival in another state of being, but of this science can give us no idea, and is content to state that death suppresses the cerebral method of consciousness forever. The mind is the culmination of the material evolution, but this can be thought of as the presence of God becoming more and more evident in his work, as a progressive spiritualization, an inspiration of matter. There is nothing on the scientific plane that enforces acceptance of such hypothese, but neither is there anything that makes possible their negation. The God who is denied by the materialists is an architect God, separated from his work, releasing a ready-made world and estranging human free will; they deny him with reason because such a concept of God is scientifically inacceptable to a science that bases everything on the evolutionary process, on the development of germinal matter, and on some spontaneous self-generating structures uninfluenced externally; man is not ready-made, but forms himself laboriously in a social environment and during the course of his struggle against nature. But this magical transcendent God is a false concept, an illogical heritage from the distant past: he has nothing in common with the Christian God, and in particular with the God of Catholic theology. It would be greatly to the credit of modern materialism, supported by science, if it were able to compel believers to disavow the idea that they are made by God, and to re-establish him in his truth. Christ is not Prometheus.

*Hylomorphism,* the doctrine held by Aristotle and St. Thomas Aquinas, was an inspirational metaphysic in agreement with the science of the period, but one whose principles are still valuable. It is remarkable that today cybernetics impels us towards a mathematical concept of the universe. Cybernetics is a theory of inspiration based on the measure of the inspiration; this concept springs directly from a science related to human language, the theory of communications, and its conjunction with the thermodynamic concept of entropy—the measure of the world's order or lack of order—leads to a synthetic view in which evolutionary history certainly appears as a process growing ever more complex, as an organization of matter in which, at the price of a loss in energy that is precisely Carnot's principle for the universe as we know it, a continuous ascent is achieved toward what is most highly organized, producing consciousness and the mind. It was the great merit of R. P. Teilhard de Chardin that he understood clearly the singularly special place held by the human phenomenon in this process, the beginning of "a new species of life." Chardin, by prophesying the vast cultural future of humanity "orbiting" in a "noosphere" in which union in love exalts human liberty shows that if "at a guess it is quite true that life makes its appearance in the universe as a simple result of the interplay of probabilities," nevertheless "the reflective psyche can never again be considered as a simple transitory by-product.... Once life had become conscious of its self, it manifests itself as a self-evolving result of the experience" demanding "the existence of a supreme Source of cosmic convergence, and one that was not only potential but real," thus disclosing at the ultimate peak of human effort the union of the eschatological dreams of the builders of the earthly city and of the defenders of the Kingdom of Heaven. To the man unsure of what happiness is, he says that "for man to be completely himself and fully alive, he must centralize himself upon self in a cultural effort, decentralizing himself from all else, to end by centralizing himself upon one greater than himself... happiness from growth, happiness from love, happiness from worship. There, in the last analysis, is the triple beatitude that theory enables us to foresee as springing from life's laws.... The whole solution of the problem of happiness is not merely to serve, but to cherish in all ways a Universe compact of love in its Evolution."

# *Index*